THE RADICAL ACCEPTANCE WORKBOOK

Transform Your Life & Free Your Mind
with the Healing Power of Self-Love & Compassion

—

Positive Lessons to Treat Anxiety, Self-Doubt,
Shame & Negative Self-Judgement

LIFEZEN PUBLICATIONS

ISBN 9789083397405 (Paperback)
ISBN 9789083397412 (Hardback)

A Gift to Our Readers!

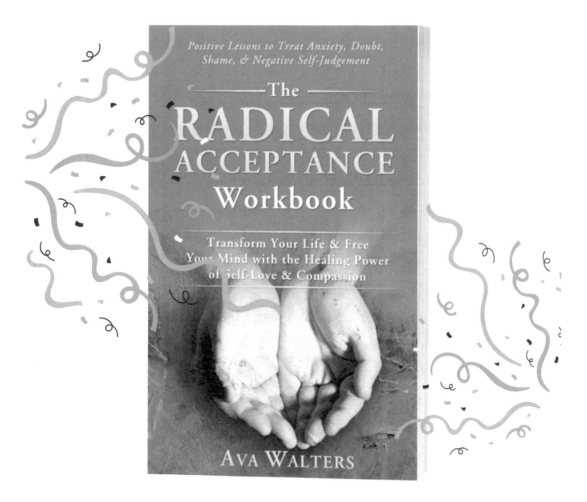

FREE DOWNLOAD ALERT!

Download and print all the worksheets
mentioned in this book. Just go to
https://life-zen.com/worksheets/rad to
get your gift, or scan the QR code on this
page.

Table of Contents

Introduction: My Journey from "a Burnout and a Breakdown" to Healing and Happiness

"One thing you can't hide - is when you're crippled inside." –
John Lennon

I was returning home from work. I had a business suit on, high heels, a smart-looking handbag on one shoulder, and a laptop case in one hand. I stepped out of my chauffeur-driven car (company-provided) and walked inside the 5-star luxurious hotel where I would stay for the next three months (company-arranged).

I imagine anyone who saw me cross that lobby that day would think I was "successful." If only they knew.

I took the elevator to the 31st floor, fished my room key out of my pocket, and as I slotted it through the door card reader, my tears started falling. Big, fat, ugly tears.

I angrily wiped my tears away, stepped in, and then, just like in previous days, the enormous dark cloud I held at bay all day engulfed me. Even now, I struggle to find the words for what I felt.

I was incredibly lonely, scared, confused, exhausted, unanchored, unbalanced, feeling inadequate... and so many other things. It was like standing still in an eerily silent place while everything inside me was howling in chaos.

At first, I thought I was suffering from extreme loneliness. I was halfway across the world from my husband, family, and friends in a country where I didn't speak the language. But then, I've been away before due to my hectic career, and I never felt this way.

I don't know how I survived the next few weeks, but I did. However, I didn't survive them unscathed. When I returned home, I was different. I was melancholic, struggling to find my footing, and tended to feel the beginnings of a panic attack whenever anything new or different was happening. I felt myself unraveling.

Unsurprisingly, my relationship with my husband was also suffering. Since I didn't understand what was going on with me, I couldn't explain things to him. My roller-coaster of moods created distance between us, and we felt increasingly disconnected.

At the back of all this was the knowledge that my family has a history of Major Depressive Disorder (MDD), and so a part of me thought that maybe I was succumbing to my inevitable fate.

In the end, knowing that depression runs in my family helped me. You see, since I knew about it, I always had an active interest in psychology, particularly anything that involved mental disorders. I would devour psychology books, keep up with the latest developments, and even attend online classes when I had the time. So, when I started to see "signs," I tried to listen to my inner voice. And it said: **I can't breathe. I need space... and time... to just breathe.** So that's what I did. I took some time off to breathe.

I saw a therapist who helped me during those initial dark and troubling weeks. Eventually, I felt it wasn't fully addressing my specific issues, whatever they were. So, I stopped after a few months and started to educate myself about Dialectic Behavior Therapy (DBT) by Dr. Marsha Linehan. (I would enroll and finish her DBT Skills certificate program later.)

DBT initially interested me because of Dr. Linehan herself. She had borderline personality disorder, and I was in absolute awe of her and her achievements in the world of psychotherapy. (I thought, *What a mountain she had to climb!*) As I became more familiar with DBT, I was exposed to the concept of **Radical Acceptance**, which was the principle that truly jumpstarted my mental healing. And as I healed, I found out who I was.

I discovered that I've been a chameleon.

As a child, I was ignored in favor of my younger twin brothers. And I was okay with that, or so I thought. I didn't realize that my coping mechanism for the lack of attention was to be exactly what other people wanted me to be. Mom always wanted a good, obedient, and quiet little girl, so I was that to her. I was "Mommy's good little helper." Dad always wanted an academic achiever, so I was that to him. I was the one who got scholarships throughout my school years. I was "Daddy's genius girl."

I want to say right now that this book is not about blaming my parents, or anyone, for that matter. I was never forced into anything. What moved my decisions was a deep-seated need to be seen, and in my young mind, to be seen meant to be what others wanted me to be.

During my last year of college, my best friend convinced me to take a temp job as a data analyst with her, so I did. I never meant to stay, but apparently, I was good at it. While my friend was let go after a few months, I was offered a permanent job, so I stayed. As the company grew and expanded globally, I grew in position, but I was never passionate about my job. I was just really good at it. Before I knew it, years had passed.

The thing is, you can only betray yourself, your inner spirit, your soul, or whatever you want to call it, for so long.

I wasn't aware that I wasn't living the life I wanted, but something inside me sensed it. After years of being a chronic people-pleaser, being a perfectionist, doing what others expected of me, and seeking approval and validation from others—my mind and body started to shut down. (Later, I would refer to this phase in my life as the time I suffered "a burnout and breakdown.")

So, Radical Acceptance taught me that I've been living my life as "someone," but not fully as myself, not 100% Ava. And since my core personality was to deny who I really was, acceptance in any form was a problem.

Whenever something at work didn't go as planned, I wouldn't accept it and swing between bouts of anger and frustration and feelings of self-doubt and inadequacy.

Whenever my husband and I had a big argument, I wouldn't accept my role in the situation and find ways to blame him.

When a friend betrayed me, I pretended the situation was "beneath me." I didn't want to address it, refusing to accept its impact on my life.

When an immediate family member became toxic and said mean things to me over lunch, I plastered a smile on my face, finished lunch(!), and went home. I was numb and in a daze for days, but I didn't want to talk about it. I told my husband it was nothing and everything would be "fine." And yes, I maintained contact with that family member for a few years.

When a small business I invested in failed, I retreated into myself, recalling and reviewing everything in my mind. I wanted to know what "I" missed and where "I" failed. (This time, I wasn't blaming others. I was self-blaming and self-gaslighting to the extreme.)

Oh, I have so many more examples than I've shared above, but I think the most damaging are the things I told myself in secret. I had this habit where if I tripped, dropped something, or forgot something, I'd silently say, "*Dumb Ava!*" (Later on, I'd realize that despite any displays of outward confidence, I suffered from extremely low self-esteem and was devoid of self-compassion.)

Over time, this constant unacceptance of myself, others, and life events was burying me deeper and deeper into misery. So, when I started to learn more about Radical Acceptance, I embraced it like a lifeline. For once, I let curiosity (not control) lead me because I was desperate to discover why I was so miserable when everything external suggested that I "should" be happy. So, what happened?

Well, it's a very weird feeling to finally get to know and understand yourself. You think you know the person you see in the mirror... but you don't (or at least not fully). People, experiences, and life put layer upon layer upon that person, and it's shocking to be stripped of all of that and see what's lying underneath. But although the journey can be unnerving, it's also very healing.

As I learned to accept myself, Radical Acceptance taught me how to practice acceptance in general. And although that can be frustrating, I realized that acceptance is just another word for "moving forward." (You'll discover why and how in the succeeding pages.)

The "short break" I took became a permanent one. To the shock of everyone around me, I chose not to return to my previous job because I accepted that it wasn't fulfilling me inside. My true passion lies in writing and psychology. I love understanding human behavior, diving into why we do the things we do, why we're in such a stage of so much stress and unhappiness today, and how we can change our lives and be happy and fulfilled. These are the pursuits that move and fulfill me. After decades, I finally met the real "Ava."

In all honesty, when I was learning and applying Radical Acceptance in my life, my only purpose then was to clear the dark clouds enveloping my existence. I never realized how much my life would be transformed!

As I radically accepted myself, others, and life in general, my self-esteem, marriage, and relationships with others improved dramatically. My happiness started radiating outwards, and people who were aware of my troubles asked me what I had done to turn my life around. When I told them about Radical Acceptance, many began to confess their own life struggles and seek my help—and so I did, doing my best to pay forward the gifts that Radical Acceptance gave my life.

Soon enough, more and more people started to get in touch and I found myself writing what I wanted to say so that I could give them a structured approach to Radical Acceptance. My simple "notes" turned to group discussions, which then turned to leading workshops. Before I knew it, I was sitting down and began constructing this book. My goal is that the ripple effect of Radical Acceptance continues to spread, touching the lives of those willing to embrace its transformative power.

So, dear reader, this book is my personal invitation to you to undertake a journey of deep self-discovery through the lens of Radical Acceptance. And in so doing, may your inner healing begin, paving the way for genuine happiness in your life.

Who Should Read This Book

This book is for anyone struggling or who knows someone having a difficult time. It's for anyone dealing with relationship challenges (personal or professional) or emotional challenges (e.g., anxiety, low self-esteem, shame, doubt, feelings of inadequacy, inner turmoil, etc.) and who wants to explore alternative therapies right from the comforts of their own home.

Goal of this Workbook

This book aims to teach you Radical Acceptance and how it can help you get to know, appreciate, and love yourself completely. It also imparts to you how Radical Acceptance can help you cope with negative and heavily unpleasant emotions so you get relief from your emotional suffering. In the end, the main purpose of this book is to help you feel better and live a life of authenticity, true happiness, and purpose—whatever that may look like for you.

How to Use This WORKBOOK

I will say this with as much compassion and honesty as possible: Please get out of your way. Try to put aside your prejudices, preferences, and natural biases. Open your mind, and welcome the ideas in the following pages.

Also, I'm a big believer in the principle that true learning takes place only when knowledge meets action. As such, this book is full of guided worksheets to help you embrace the concepts mentioned in this book.

Your Feelings and Experiences are Valid

During my journey, I would get a bit peeved when people "knew better" than what I was feeling or experiencing; many people gave their opinion (judgment) rather than empathy. So, here's my message to you:

Your truth matters. Your feelings are valid. Your experiences hold significance. Your trauma deserves attention. Please don't let anyone undermine your reality or your voice because you have the absolute right to experience and express your feelings without judgment or dismissal. Embrace your truth and honor your journey no matter how long it takes.

Kindness

Please remember that your Radical Acceptance journey is not a race but a gradual growth and healing process. You might experience ups and downs, progress and setbacks, and struggle with ideas that go against your current beliefs. That's all okay! Be kind and patient during challenging moments because they're part of the journey. Remember to treat yourself with the same kindness and empathy you would offer to a dear friend.

So, dear reader, just at a time when you may want to shut everything and everyone out and deny the chaos and absurdities of this current world, I ask you to open up and embrace acceptance instead. Will you take this step with me?

Ava Watters

Amazon Bestselling Author
Radical Accepter

Part I: Understanding Radical Acceptance

"Accept yourself, love yourself, and keep moving forward. If you want to fly, you have to give up what weighs you down."
— Roy T. Bennett

In the context of "Radical Acceptance," the term "radical" means complete, thorough, and profound. No *ifs* and *buts*. So Radical Acceptance is an all-embracing and unwavering form of acknowledgment—of yourself, others, situations, etc.

Radical Acceptance encourages accepting reality AS IS without resistance, denial, or judgment, even in the face of challenging situations.

RADICAL ACCEPTANCE

IT'S RAINING!

IT'S RAINING!

No......!
It's going to be a gloomy day.
Well, I can't do any of my plans now.
Why is this happening to me?
When will this rain end?!
My day's ruined!
It's always raining. I hate this place.
This is so unfair!

Yep!

Radical Acceptance encourages accepting reality AS IS without resistance, denial, or judgment, even in the face of challenging situations.

Now, you might be wondering WHY you should radically accept even unpleasant feelings or events, and here's the answer: **to free yourself**.

Imagine painful or challenging situations like having the *flu*. When you're sick, you may think thoughts such as:

I have so many things to do! Why do I have the flu now?
I have travel plans. What if this doesn't clear up by then?

I wonder who gave this to me?!

This is Robin's fault. They had the flu and still attended my party.

I should've known better! Why did I have to go out without a coat?

If you suffer from anxiety, you might even think *OMG, this is COVID.*

Round and round your thoughts go. Amidst all this ruminating, you're essentially *nurturing* your flu (the problem). When we give our problems so much attention, we get stuck in that situation and prolong our suffering.

Radical Acceptance helps you let go of your pain and suffering and focus on taking action to change your situation. So, in the flu scenario above, skip the negative and unhelpful thoughts and ruminations and focus on what you can do to get better instead (e.g., taking medication, drinking plenty of water, getting enough rest, etc.).

So, think of it like this: the longer you deny or refuse to accept something, the longer you'll suffer from it. The sooner you accept, the sooner you can move on to feeling better.

Unacceptance is marinating in a negative situation.

Acceptance is the first step to getting out of one.

Chapter 1. The Foundations of Radical Acceptance

Radical Acceptance isn't "new." It draws from Eastern philosophies like Buddhism and Taoism, which stress accepting the present moment without judgment, cultivating inner peace, and embracing the impermanence of life.

However, as I mentioned at the start of this book, I was introduced to this concept while studying Dialectical Behavior Therapy (DBT), developed by Dr. Marsha M. Linehan in the 1980s.[1] DBT, which incorporates the principles of acceptance and change, emphasizes the importance of Radical Acceptance as a fundamental component of mental healing.

More recently, mindfulness-based approaches, such as Mindfulness-Based Stress Reduction (MBSR) and Acceptance and Commitment Therapy (ACT), have further emphasized the significance of accepting one's thoughts and emotions without judgment.

All of the above practices have highlighted how acceptance without judgment enhances emotional well-being and resilience.

Misconceptions About Radical Acceptance

Even though Radical Acceptance has been around for a while, many people find it difficult to embrace because of all the misconceptions surrounding it. So, let's first clarify what it is and what it's not.

Radical Acceptance IS NOT: Agreement, approval, or consent.
You're not agreeing to anything, saying you're okay with something or someone, or giving consent. You're just acknowledging that a situation exists or has happened.

Radical Acceptance IS NOT: Denial or avoidance.

Radical Acceptance is embracing truth or reality AS IS. You're not trying to deny or avoid difficult situations or negative feelings. You're accepting your awareness of them to find ways to cope effectively.

Radical Acceptance IS NOT: Giving up or giving in.

Accepting a situation doesn't mean you don't want things to improve. When you accept something, it doesn't mean you want it to happen again or that you want the situation to stay that way. It's also not about giving yourself or anyone a "pass." It's acknowledging and embracing the truth of a situation, including all associated emotions.

Radical Acceptance IS NOT: Inaction.

When difficult situations occur, you're not saying you will lie down and be "okay" with it. You acknowledge what happened because it already happened, and you cannot undo the past. Remember, taking action belongs in the future.

Radical Acceptance IS NOT: Suppressing or ignoring emotions.

Radical Acceptance is about allowing ALL feelings to exist. It's about enjoying moments of happiness and acknowledging moments of pain without judgment.

Radical Acceptance IS NOT: Downplaying or trivializing.

This concept doesn't involve underestimating the significance of challenging or distressing experiences. Instead, it supports a deep and nonjudgmental recognition of these experiences, helping you understand how complicated they are and how they make you feel.

Radical Acceptance IS NOT: Dwelling on the past (regrets) or obsessing over the future (fears).

It's about living and feeling the present moment. If you keep reliving the past or are anxious about the future, you're robbing yourself of the present moment. Radical Acceptance is about living in "NOW."

Radical Acceptance IS NOT: Being indifferent or not caring.

Often, being indifferent, detached, or uncaring about something is a sign of deep pain. So much despair that whether you fully realize it or not, you deny the situation by outwardly saying or showing that you don't care. Radical Acceptance is the opposite. It promotes full acceptance of the problem and the pain it's causing, not because you want to be hurt but because you want to be healed.

Radical Acceptance IS NOT: About others.

Your reality is unique to you. As such, you cannot accept for others, only for yourself.

At this stage, I ask you to rethink and redefine the word "acceptance" in your life to:

ACCEPTANCE IS
ACKNOWLEDGING REALITY <u>AS IS</u>

And when it comes to Radical Acceptance:

RADICAL ACCEPTANCE IS
ACKNOWLEDGING REALITY <u>AS IS</u>
WITHOUT RESISTANCE, DENIAL OR JUDGMENT

The Benefits of Radical Acceptance

Radical Acceptance is the most liberating concept I've ever come across. At first, I met it with a bit of skepticism (hmmm...), a dash of fear (can I do this?), and loads of uncertainty (not sure about this...). But as I learned and practiced it in my life, I just felt "lighter." Here are some of the key benefits Radical Acceptance offers:

Reduces Stress: Radical Acceptance can help you feel less stressed and anxious. When you accept things AS IS, I can't tell you just how much pressure is taken off your shoulders! No more agonizing about the *this* or *that*, or the *why's* or *why not's* of a situation. Once you accept it, dealing with it gets easier.

Promotes Personal Growth: Radical Acceptance can lead to personal growth and transformation because it fosters a journey of self-discovery and development. It encourages you to face yourself and answer questions such as, *What makes me happy?* Or *What brings me joy?*

When you ask yourself these questions, DON'T be surprised to come up with answers far from your current reality. For example, say that you're a customer service rep, but you used to like baking. In this instance, find ways to bring back baking into your life.

Enhances Self-Compassion: Radical Acceptance encourages deep self-compassion. As you go through the coming pages, you'll go through a journey of self-acceptance and understanding. And in doing so, you'll learn to be kinder and more empathetic with yourself.

Improves Relationships: Practicing Radical Acceptance can enhance relationships by fostering acceptance of others AS IS (instead of what you want or expect them to be). This nurtures genuine understanding and empathy towards others, creating a more harmonious relationship.

Stimulates Emotional Resilience: Radical Acceptance fosters emotional resilience by enabling you to navigate challenging situations with greater ease and inner strength.

Reduces Emotional Suffering: Radical Acceptance can lead to freedom from emotional stress and suffering because often, we unknowingly put these pressures on ourselves by agonizing, or what I call "marinating," in our problems. By unwaveringly accepting reality, even if that reality is uncomfortable or painful, we let go of the need for control and perfection and embrace life's imperfections. From there, we can move forward and work to find solutions to make an unpleasant situation better.

Prevents Self-Gaslighting: Self-gaslighting refers to the act of doubting or questioning your own thoughts, feelings, or experiences, often leading to a distorted perception of reality. It involves internalizing self-doubt to the point where you may dismiss your own feelings or memories, creating a sense of confusion or invalidation within yourself.

If you've ever said any of the following statements to yourself, you might be self-gaslighting. Please go over the list and check the ones that resonate with you.

[ ] Maybe it's all just in my head; everybody says it is.
[ ] I'm overreacting. I'm sure they didn't mean it.
[ ] Oh, you're right. I must be misremembering.

[ ] Why do I make everything worse?!

[ ] It's my fault; I always mess things up.

[ ] No, no, I have no opinions.

[ ] I must be imagining things; it couldn't have happened that way.

[ ] I have no right to complain.

[ ] I'm not good enough for _____.

[ ] I must have done something to provoke this.

[ ] Why do I always cause problems?!

[ ] I'm just being paranoid; there's nothing to worry about.

[ ] Maybe they're right; I'm not capable of anything.

[ ] I'm too much trouble for others; I should just keep quiet.

[ ] I shouldn't be upset. I make myself a target of jokes all the time.

Self-gaslighting statements undermine your sense of self-worth and reality. Radical Acceptance helps prevent self-gaslighting by teaching you to accept, understand, love, and be proud of yourself. It promotes truth and honesty and, in doing so, helps you see things AS IS without judgment or self-doubt. This practice allows you to establish firm boundaries and trust your perceptions, making it more challenging for others to manipulate your sense of reality.

The Aspects of Radical Acceptance

Radical Acceptance is not a switch you can just turn "On." To make it your second nature, you must cultivate the following qualities:

Mindfulness is nurturing presence in "now." This means not living in the past or the future but living fully in the present moment. (See Chapter 2. Mindfulness: Living in NOW.)

Self-awareness is cultivating a deep understanding of your thoughts, feelings, and behaviors and practicing present-moment awareness. (See Chapter 3. Self-Awareness: I See ME.)

Non-Judgment is approaching situations and experiences with an open and non-critical mindset, allowing understanding, empathy, and facts (not assumptions or opinions) to prevail. (See Chapter 4: Non-Judgment: Breaking Free from the Chains of Criticism.)

Embracing Imperfection is realizing and accepting that perfection is unattainable. Instead, one should focus on the beauty and growth of embracing your flaws and imperfections. See Chapter 5: Embracing Imperfection.)

Letting Go of Control is releasing the need to control external situations or outcomes and instead focusing on developing inner peace and resilience. (See Chapter 6: Letting Go of Control.)

Radical Willingness is cultivating a mindset of openness and willingness to experience life as it unfolds without resistance or attachment to specific outcomes. (See Chapter 7: Radical Willingness.)

Radical Self-Acceptance is learning to embrace your entire being. It's about fostering a genuine connection with your true self and being at peace with who you are and intend to be. (See Chapter 8: Radical Self-Acceptance)

A note about vulnerability:

As you read this book, you might feel vulnerable at certain moments. That's understandable and perfectly okay. Radical Acceptance is not easy; it asks you to embrace your identity, experiences, thoughts, and emotions without any defense mechanisms or shields, which, like me, I'm sure you've been putting up around you for years. So, Radical Acceptance might initially feel uncomfortable or unsettling, but know that this vulnerability is a natural part of self-discovery and emotional healing.

However, please note that being open and vulnerable DOES NOT give anyone license to cause you pain or harm. Ensure that your vulnerabilities are respected and protected by setting and enforcing boundaries. For example, suppose you feel vulnerable and want to be alone, and a family member drops by unannounced. If this is not helpful, say that you need space and ask the person to drop by some other time. Create a safe space for yourself so you can maintain a sense of emotional security when feeling vulnerable.

Part II: Bringing Acceptance Into Your Life

"The secret of change is to focus all of your energy, not on fighting the old, but on building the new."— Socrates

"Radical Acceptance" seems simple. But as I learned more about it and practiced it, I realized that even though the concept is easy to grasp, it's difficult to apply because, as adults, we've put up many walls and masks to protect ourselves.

Radical Acceptance asks us to *unlearn* a lifetime of habits. But then again, if these habits, beliefs, and behaviors are not making us happy or are even harming us... why should we keep on doing them?

It's like grabbing a hammer and hitting ourselves repeatedly because we haven't learned to put the hammer down.

So, let's put the hammer down....

Chapter 2. Mindfulness: Living in NOW

Many people confuse mindfulness with meditation, and that's one of the reasons people don't try it. (*Me, sitting down cross-legged and chanting "Om" for endless minutes?! No way!*) So here's the difference: mindfulness is a quality; meditation is a practice.

Mindfulness is a state of mind; it's something you are.
Meditation is a practice; it's something you do.

So, what IS mindfulness? It's a state of full awareness of the present moment. You're not thinking about anything that has happened (past) or anything you need to do in the next moment (future). You're simply in a state of NOW.

Mindfulness is not easy in today's world because we lead busy lives. We're used to multi-tasking, and thanks to social media and 24/7 news, we're overly stimulated and stressed.

We're also constantly distracted. And although social media and digital technology are partly to blame, research conducted by Harvard psychologists showed that we're so distracted because we engage in constant "mind wandering."[2] Yep, we like to time travel through our minds.

It's waiting in line and thinking about dinner. It's having dinner and thinking about how badly you want to shower and sleep. It's getting in bed and agonizing about all the work you must do tomorrow. And how about that "out of body experience" where someone's right in front of you, talking to you, and the minute they stop and stare at you, you go, "*I'm sorry, what did you say?*" So, if you really think about it, you're hardly ever in the present moment.

Constant mind wandering makes us unhappy, and it can even lead to depression[3] because our focus is on what's NOT happening. To be fair, evolution made us this way.

Our ancestors always had to be on high alert and think about any potential (not present) threat as a way to survive. Unfortunately, even though we're no longer faced with the danger of being eaten alive by predators, there's undoubtedly more stress than ever on the human mind in the form of emotional stress.[4] So, how do you focus more and wander less? Mindfulness holds the key.

When it comes to mindfulness, breath awareness is important. Now, you might be thinking, well, that's easy! Is it?

Most people are *shallow breathers* or *fast breathers*, inhaling through the nose or mouth, trapping air in the chest, and then puffing it out. This means that air doesn't reach your diaphragms.

Daily stress has made humans shallow breathers.[5] It contributes to a host of health problems such as chronic stress, anxiety, inability to think fast, inability to experience quality sleep, fatigue, memory loss, and many others. In contrast, *deep breathing* or *diaphragmatic breathing* promotes less feelings of breathlessness, a more relaxed mind, and better overall well-being.[6]

Deep breathing is an important element of mindfulness because it is an anchor for cultivating present-moment awareness. When you breathe deeply and with intention, you stimulate your body's relaxation response.[7] This process encourages you to shift your focus away from racing thoughts and daily distractions toward only one thing: your breath.

After anchoring yourself to "now," start paying attention to what's happening outside you—one thing at a time.

For example, grab the FIRST object you see. Next, describe it. Don't give any opinion (e.g., *I don't like this shape*); just use descriptive words (e.g., *It's round*). Next, participate mindfully. How are you holding the object? Are you clutching it tightly or holding it loosely? Are you keeping it with one hand or both? Are you holding it at the top, bottom, or middle?

As you can assume, mindfulness doesn't entertain the word "rushed." It's about deliberately taking your time and creating mental space to focus on what's happening inside and outside yourself at any moment. As you go through this book, you'll realize how mindfulness makes you happier, more deliberate, and more empathic.

Worksheet 1: Counting Breath Practice

Just like any new skill, it helps to gradually ease into it. So, for mindfulness beginners, please try this counting breath practice first.

Step 1. Sit or lie down in a comfortable position.

Step 2. Say "One" and inhale slowly through your nose.

Step 3. Say "Two" and exhale slowly through your mouth.

Step 4. Repeat steps 2 and 3 until you reach "Ten."

In all likelihood, somewhere along the way, you'll get lost, distracted, and forget your counting before you reach "Ten." Whenever that happens, start over with "One."

If you find yourself at, say, "18" without realizing how you got there, then you're still not anchored to the present moment. In this case, start over with "One."

This exercise is not about achieving "10," but the mindful journey of getting there. You must be fully aware of EACH of the 10 breaths you take.

Important: Struggling to reach 10 with full awareness? That's okay. Take a break and try again later. Remember, be kind, and have patience with yourself.

Worksheet 2: Mindful Deep Belly Breathing

Deep belly breathing, or diaphragmatic breathing, is a simple yet powerful tool easily incorporated into your daily routine to promote relaxation, reduce stress, and enhance overall well-being. Regular practice can help cultivate a sense of inner peace and emotional balance.

Step 1. Set a timer for 5 minutes.

Step 2. Sit or lie down in a comfortable position.

Step 3. Place one hand on your chest and the other on your abdomen, just below your rib cage.

Step 4. Inhale slowly. Close your eyes and begin to inhale slowly through your nose. As you inhale, focus on expanding your abdomen, feeling it rise as your lungs fill with air. Breathe deeply enough that you feel your abdomen rise more than your chest.

Step 5. Hold your breath briefly at the top of your inhale, holding your breath for a moment without straining.

Step 6. Exhale slowly. Let your breath out slowly and gently through your mouth or nose. As you exhale, focus on allowing your abdomen to fall naturally, feeling it lower as the air leaves your lungs.

Step 7. Repeat steps 3-5. Continue this breathing pattern for several minutes, maintaining a slow and steady rhythm. Pay attention to the sensation of your breath as it travels in and out of your body, keeping your focus solely on the act of breathing.

Step 8. As you practice deep belly breathing, notice any areas of stress or tension in your body. Release any tension you feel with each exhale.

Step 9. When the timer goes off, slowly open your eyes and maintain a sense of calm and relaxation. Notice any changes in your body and mind, such as the release of stress, the relaxation of muscles, a sense that time has slowed down, etc.

Worksheet 3: Mindful Observation Using Your Five Senses

Breathing exercises help you focus. They train you to become FULLY AWARE of ONE act (i.e., the act of breathing). The mindful observation exercise below takes you a step further. You're not just focused on breathing now. This practice aims to help you cultivate present-moment awareness and deepen your connection with your surroundings. By focusing your attention on the details of your environment—*without judgment or interpretation*—you can become more mindful.

Step 1. Find a quiet and comfortable space to sit or stand without distractions.

Step 2. Pick an object within your surroundings to serve as the target of this observation exercise. It could be a natural object, artwork, or anything that captures your attention.

Step 3. Engage your senses. Start by taking a few deep belly breaths to center yourself and focus your attention on the present moment. Next, use your senses, one at a time, to carefully observe the item you chose.

Step 4. What do you see? Observe the visual details of the object, paying attention to its shape, color, texture, and any intricate patterns or features. Note how the light reflects off the object and how shadows form around it.

Step 5. What textures do you feel? If possible, gently touch the object and notice its surface, temperature, and any unique sensations it suggests. (For example, if it's cool to your touch, it may prompt a slight chill in you.) Focus on the tactile experience and the physical sensations that arise from your interaction with the object.

Step 6. What do you hear? Shift your focus to the sounds near and far in your environment. If the object you chose makes a sound, bring it closer to your ear and focus on what you're hearing. Can you describe the sound? Does the sound remind you of something? If the item doesn't make a sound, extend your focus and notice any surrounding sounds, such as the rustle of leaves, wind against your window pane, a car passing by, etc. Allow these sounds to come and go without attachment or judgment.

Step 7. What do you smell? Pay attention to any scents or aromas present in your environment. Take a few deep breaths and notice any subtle or distinct smells you encounter, whether pleasant, unpleasant, or neutral.

Step 8. What do you taste in your mouth? Perhaps there's the lingering taste of candy or coffee. Try not to engage with the taste; just take note of it.

Step 9. After engaging your five senses, **acknowledge any thoughts, emotions, or physical sensations that arose during this exercise**. For example, how often did you tend to label or interpret your observations? This is normal, especially if this is your first time trying this exercise. Whenever this occurs, gently guide your focus back to the sensory experience.

Step 10. After several minutes of mindful observation, take a moment to reflect on your experience. Think about how the exercise heightened your awareness and deepened your connection with the present moment.

Recommendation: Do this exercise at least once a day until you observe items in an almost "detached" way. Use your senses one at a time and avoid labeling, interpreting, or forming an opinion about what you observe. (Don't observe people yet. Later in this book, there'll be a specific exercise for that.)

Worksheet 4: Notice+Shift+Rewire

Still engaging in a lot of mind-wandering? This Notice-Shift-Rewire (NSR) mindfulness exercise, commonly associated with mindfulness-based cognitive therapy (MBCT) and mindfulness-based stress reduction (MBSR) programs, can help you.[8]

Step 1. Notice

Notice moments when you become "lost in thought." This may be hard to do because, often, you're already in the middle of your mind wandering before you become aware you're doing it. However, you know who you are, so where, when, or with whom do you tend to mind wander?

For example, do you get lost in thoughts under the shower? If so, you might want to try "stepping under the shower" as a cue. It's like telling your mind, *Oh, I tend to mind wander here.* This simple way of putting yourself on notice will help with the next step.

You may also have a "tell" when your mind is wandering. For example, do you tend to look out the window when you mind-travel? If so, make windows your cue.

Step 2. Shift

After noticing your mind wandering, gently redirect your attention to the present moment. This can be focusing on your breath or throwing yourself fully into what you're doing (e.g., showering, holding a cup of coffee, writing an email, etc.) During idle moments like waiting in line, do Mindful Observation Using Your Five Senses (page 27) to help you re-focus.

Step 3. Rewire

The final step is reinforcing this new present-awareness way of thinking by engaging in it for at least 15 to 30 seconds. Yes, it doesn't take that long to rewire the brain to form a new habit, but you do need to do it often (e.g., at least 3x a day for at least a week). Luckily, you can do this NSR exercise anytime, anywhere!

So, what will happen when you lessen mind wandering and become more mindful?

For one, you'll be shocked at everything you've been missing because of your inattentiveness to the present moment. Second, you'll feel less stressed because you're not constantly worrying about *what was* or *what could be*. You'll feel more alive because you're more connected to what's happening in your life—in real-time.

Meditation Sucks!

So, mindfulness is a character trait, and meditation is one of the ways you can develop it. Ergo, it's in your best interest to engage in meditation. But it sucks, you say.

I have a confession. The first time I tried to meditate, I couldn't do it. I played some relaxing music on YouTube, comfortably sat down, and after a few breaths, I was already thinking of all the work I had to do. So, I stopped and stood up.

The next day, I tried again and gave up again. I don't remember how often I tried and stopped until I had this sobering thought: "Wow, Ava, you can't control your *mind?!*" And it bothered me, that thought.

How am I functioning during the day if I can't control my thoughts and quiet my mind? "Scatter-brained" is a trait I wasn't aspiring to. How can I make "sound decisions" if I can't focus or if I'm not fully aware of what's happening around me? This startling insight changed how I looked at meditation, and I started to think, "*I'm not giving this enough time. I just don't know how to meditate... yet.*"

The more I became open to meditation, the easier it became. Soon enough, I stopped looking at it as a time-waster and started to treat it as a "mind spa." I meditate in the mornings to slowly wake myself up and start my day by filling my mind with positive and intentional thoughts. When I'm feeling stressed, I meditate to release tension. When I'm feeling lost, I meditate to ground myself. Sometimes, I just meditate to give myself a little "mind reboot."

As I talked to family, friends, and people undergoing their own healing journeys, I discovered various other reasons why people think meditation sucks. Following are some of these reasons and why you should perhaps rethink them.

Meditation is boring.

Quick! What do you think meditation looks like? Do you have a picture of sitting down cross-legged and being quiet (or saying "om")? If you want to, you can do that, but plenty of meditation techniques are available. My personal favorite is to do a Walking Meditation (page 35). Still, there's also body scan or grounding meditation, guided meditation (following the audio instructions), Transcendental Meditation (TM) (using mantras), movement meditation (e.g., yoga), and others.

By the way, have you done Worksheets 1 and 2? If you have, you have meditated already; those worksheets are examples of breath awareness meditation.

I don't have time.

I get it. We all lead busy lives. However, meditation is highly adaptable and can be tailored to suit your schedule. Moreover, meditation doesn't have to be long at all. Even just a few minutes of mindfulness can yield tangible benefits.[9] Can't you prioritize yourself for even just 10 minutes?

Meditation doesn't do anything.

Countless studies indicate that meditation provides emotional, physical, and mental benefits.[10] However, since we don't see these benefits immediately (no instant gratification here!), we think meditation doesn't do anything. So, please give it time. The benefits of meditation manifest themselves gradually.

Meditation is a religious practice, and I'm not religious.

Although meditation has its roots in Hinduism and Buddhism, it doesn't need to be linked to religion. Instead, think of meditation as a link to YOU, an exercise in stillness, self-observation, and just being.

I'm not comfortable with silence.

Busy lives. Turbulent thoughts. Chaotic emotions. Rush, rush, rush! This is our normal. So much so that meditation, stillness, and silence can be so uncomfortable. However, please note that the goal of meditation is not to eliminate thoughts but to observe them without judgment and that even very brief moments of mental stillness can profoundly affect your stress and emotional well-being.

I don't need meditation in my life.

Science shows that meditation reduces stress[11], prevents illness[12], helps with weight control[13], improves sleep[14], enhances memory and other mental capacities[15], etc. Don't you want any of these benefits in your life?

Years ago, someone told me that mindfulness and meditation are difficult because, in truth, it's hard to be alone. Ouch! It's hard to give up the screens, the distractions, and the noise because silence is so uncomfortable and deafening.

So, I encourage you to try mindfulness and meditation by leaving you with this thought: BE CURIOUS.

BE CURIOUS

about how you can be the master of your own mind.

BE CURIOUS

about the specific benefits you will reap.

BE CURIOUS

about what you've been missing during the times you

haven't been fully present in the moment.

BE CURIOUS

about the profound sense of relaxation, peace, and clarity

that can come from mindfulness.

Worksheet 5: Walking Meditation

Being outdoors in nature does wonders for your stress levels and overall health.[16,17,18] I guess that's why walking meditations are one of my favorites. Here's how you can try it:

Step 1. Find a quiet and safe outdoor location to walk without distractions or interruptions.

Step 2. Stand still for a few moments. Take a couple of deep breaths to ground yourself and be aware of your body and the surrounding environment.

Step 3. Set an intention for your walk. Examples:

I'm going to take a walk to reduce my stress.
I'm going to take a walk to calm my emotions.
I'm going to take a walk to practice mindfulness.

Step 4. Begin your walk. Start walking slowly and comfortably, standing straight, and allowing your arms to hang naturally by your sides.

Step 5. After a minute or two of walking, focus all your attention on yourself, one body part at a time. Start from the top of your head, working your way down to your feet. Examples:

My head feels heavy. Let me de-stress that a bit with a few deep breaths.
My shoulders are tensed. Let me relax them now.
Work your way down to the sensation of your feet touching the ground,
noticing the shifting pressure and movements with each step.

Step 6. Practice mindful awareness of your surroundings. Pay attention to the sights, sounds, and smells around you, fully immersing yourself in the present moment and embracing the sensory experiences.

Step 7. Next, practice breath and step synchronization. Coordinate your breathing with your steps, inhaling slowly and deeply as you take a few strides and exhaling gradually as you continue walking. Focus on the rhythm of your breath and steps, allowing them to harmonize and create a sense of flow and continuity.

Note: If you don't have much time, skip steps 5-7 and just do Counting Breath Practice (page 24) as you walk. Don't rush your steps! Be deliberate and cultivate a focused awareness of each step you take.

Step 8. When you're at the last leg of your walk, reflect on the simple act of walking in peace and the privilege of being able to practice mindfulness. Express gratitude for your body's ability to move and the nature surrounding you.

Step 9. Gradually slow your pace as you approach the end of your walk, allowing yourself to come to a natural stop. (Again, no rushing!) Intentionally delay "next." If you start thinking about what you need to do next, walk even slower and breathe deeply.

Step 10. When you're done, take a moment to stand still and pull that sense of calmness and awareness deeper inside you, intending to continue mindfulness for the rest of your day.

*Radical Acceptance requires Mindfulness
because you cannot fully accept something you're not fully aware of.*

Mindfulness helps you focus and be 100% present in the moment. Only when you slow down and be mindful can you really understand and see what's inside you and around you. Only then can you fully accept.

Chapter 3. Self-Awareness: I See ME

As you've learned, mindfulness is about complete awareness. This chapter focuses on directing that awareness towards yourself.

Self-awareness means understanding yourself—completely. It's knowing your feelings, thoughts, motives, and why you do what you do (behavior). It's about being attuned to yourself and how you perceive yourself in various situations.

Many of us would like to believe that we know ourselves, but I think we only know bits and pieces, and mostly only the good parts, because it's hard to accept the not-so-flattering ones. Some only see their not-so-good qualities, unable or unwilling to accept the good they have inside them. Self-awareness sees both. It's the ability to completely see and accept who you are—good and bad, strengths and weaknesses, head to toe, left to right, and inside-out.

Here's something I wasn't fully aware about myself.

We were in Canada for a family vacation. My husband and I booked two hotel suites, one for us and one for my mom and younger brothers. My husband was filming as I showed my mom around her suite. In the video, my voice was very high-pitched! NEVER have I envisioned myself having such a voice. A few minutes later, the video showed me talking to my brothers and husband as he was filming, and my voice was audibly softer, more "normal."

After watching the video, I realized something about myself for the first time. I unconsciously, excitedly, raised my voice when speaking to my mom because I wanted her to be pleased with her room. In that startling moment of self-awareness, plenty of previous situations flashed through my mind in which I desperately tried to please her.

As I realized this, I began to ask, *What else? What else am I doing that I'm not fully aware of?*

Mind you, not everything will be revealed in one go. You see, self-awareness is an ongoing process of introspection and reflection. It takes time to gain insight into your own patterns of thinking and behaving.

I'd also like to stress that self-awareness is not just reflecting on *previous* situations. Ideally, you're self-aware *in the moment.* You can see and note your feelings, thoughts, motives, and why you do the things you do (behavior)—as you do them.

Now, you might be asking, *Why do I need to understand myself completely?* Well, how can you expect others to do so if you don't? Isn't it a BIG ASK for others to "get" you if you don't "get" yourself?

You might also be wondering, *Why do I need to be aware of my thoughts, emotions, and actions as I do them?* Because wherever you are, you're helping shape your current situation.

Imagine you're in a team meeting at work, and a colleague suggests a new idea. You don't agree, and you're about to say something sarcastic. However, if you're self-aware, you realize *in that moment* that you shouldn't react that way; it's neither compassionate nor professional.

This self-awareness allows you to understand how your response might affect the meeting; either you're fostering open discussion and teamwork or creating an atmosphere of resistance.

Here are other reasons why it's important to cultivate self-awareness:

You'll see patterns in your behavior.

Self-awareness enables you to recognize recurring thoughts, emotions, and behaviors patterns. Knowing these patterns will give insight into why you say, think, and behave like you do.

You'll understand your triggers.

By becoming more self-aware, you can figure out what situations or triggers induce strong emotional reactions or resistance in you. And if you know your triggers, you can avoid them, relieving yourself of potential pain and emotional suffering.

You'll be kinder to yourself.

We're usually our own worst critic. We're often ready and willing to see what's "wrong" with us. Self-awareness helps us see the good in us and the good we do. And when we're being impatient, annoying, or downright obnoxious, being self-aware of that is in and of itself a good thing because then we can shift our behavior.

You'll evolve into your authentic self.

Who are you? Do you truly know? As the years go by, many factors greatly influence our lives. We adapt, we change, we transform... but into what? Self-awareness helps cultivate a deeper understanding of who you are right now; not who you were and want to be. Only from a point of pure self-awareness can you decide if you're living life as the real you.

You'll see your relationships improve.

Self-awareness is not just about knowing what's happening inside you. It also entails being fully aware of what you say and think and how you behave towards others.

You'll make better decisions.

Have you ever been so mad that you blurted out something that you immediately regretted? Have you ever been so bored and lonely that you did something you shouldn't have? We've all been there. Emotions drive most of human behavior.[19] But if you're mindfully self-aware, you can give yourself that time and mental space to THINK your emotions through so you can cope with the situation better and make better decisions.

So, self-awareness is about accepting who you are, warts and all. And it's about being aware of what you're thinking, saying, and doing in any situation. It's like being fully awake and seeing yourself as your day unfolds.

Oh, I'm looking at my watch again. I better stop before my boss thinks I don't want to be here.

I'm clenching my hands. I'm upset. It's okay; this situation is beyond my control. Breathe. Breathe. Breathe.

Ready to be more self-aware? Here's a guide to get you started:

Step 1. Engage in mindfulness.

If you remember, mindfulness cultivates present-moment awareness. So, if you're mindful, it's easier to be self-aware. Imagine being extremely angry with someone. Mindfulness gives you that mental space to tell yourself:

Okay, I'm really upset right now. (self-awareness)
Let me calm down before I say something that might worsen this situation.

Step 2. Start journaling.

Maintain a journal to record your daily experiences, emotions, and reactions. This will help you better understand your behavioral patterns and triggers. **Important:** DO NOT judge your feelings or experiences; just describe what happened.

If journaling is not your thing, find a quiet moment at the end of your day, close your eyes, and self-reflect. Explore your thoughts, feelings, and experiences without judgment.

Step 3. Step outside your comfort zone.

Trying something new always brings out the unexpected. Engage in new activities or hobbies that challenge your perspectives and help you discover previously unknown aspects of yourself.

Step 4. Develop strategies for managing your emotions better.

As you become more self-aware, which emotions tend to get the better of you, and how do you normally cope with them?

For example, do you tend to emotionally eat when you're sad? If so, look for healthier ways to deal with sadness, such as investing more time in offline friendships, learning yoga, playing feel-good tunes on Spotify, etc.

Step 5. Ask others for feedback.

Let's face it. When it comes to yourself, you may be biased. So, when you feel strong and courageous enough, ask people you trust to provide constructive feedback and insights into your strengths and areas for growth.

Step 6. Set a personal goal.

As you get to know yourself better, identify clear and achievable personal goals that reflect your *values*.

For example, let's say you realize that you have a deep passion for environmental conservation and sustainability. In this scenario, you might aim to volunteer for local conservation initiatives, use more eco-friendly products in your home, etc. By aligning your goals with your values, you live a life that stays true to your authentic self.

Worksheet 6: Self-Awareness Exploration

Use this worksheet as a guide to explore and enhance your self-awareness. Complete each step mindfully, allowing yourself to delve deeper into your thoughts, emotions, and behaviors.

Step 1. Think of a recent unpleasant situation or undesired outcome.

Example: A misunderstanding with some friends. We discussed having a dinner date, but there was some miscommunication and I didn't arrive on the date. My friends got mad because they thought I blew them off, and I got angry because no one confirmed the dinner plans with me.

What situation did you choose?

_____

_____

_____

_____

_____

_____

Step 2. What did you feel?

Reflect on your emotional state regarding the situation and write down your feelings, acknowledging their presence without judgment or censorship.

Example: I felt annoyed and left out.

What were your emotions?

_____

_____

_____

_____

_____

_____

Step 3. What thoughts did you have?

Observe your thoughts about the situation without attachment, noticing any recurring thought patterns or themes. Write down any predominant thoughts that come to mind, acknowledging their presence.

Example: I thought it was incredibly unfair to assume I would just know when and where we were supposed to have dinner.

What were your thoughts?

_____

_____

_____

_____

_____

_____

Step 4. What did you do?

Write what you did as a result of the situation.

Example: When they texted me that they were at the restaurant waiting for me, I replied sarcastically. Something like, "Wow, you guys are absolute rock stars at communicating!" After that, I no longer replied to their text messages.

What were your actions?

_____
_____
_____
_____
_____
_____
_____

Step 5. Practice self-awareness.

Reflect on your behaviors and actions, and ask yourself what you would have done differently. If possible, identify any habits or actions you frequently engage in, both positive and negative.

Example: Looking back, I could've sent a quick WhatsApp message asking about the dinner plans. I didn't have to wait for someone to contact me first. Patterns? I guess I tend to shut down and become uncommunicable when annoyed. I have a pattern of giving the cold shoulder and ghosting people when I'm pissed.

What have you noticed about yourself?

_____
_____
_____
_____
_____
_____

Step 6. What happened after you acted out your thoughts and emotions?

Reflect on what happened as a direct result of your behavior.

Example: After ghosting my friends, I didn't hear from them for days. They thought I was childish, and I thought they were mean. All in all, it didn't help our friendship.

What happened?

_____

_____

_____

_____

_____

_____

Step 7. Did the situation trigger anything in you?

Why do you think the situation evoked such a strong emotional or behavioral response from you? Write down any triggers you noticed.

Example: The situation triggered feelings of being left out and excluded.

What are your triggers?

_____

_____

_____

_____

_____

_____

Step 8. Reflect.

Use the space below to write a journal entry, exploring your thoughts, emotions, and behaviors in-depth. Consider how your thoughts and emotions influenced your behaviors and how external factors impact your internal state.

Example: I guess my feelings of being left-out made me send that sarcastic message to my friends.

_____

_____

_____

_____

_____

_____

Step 9. Set personal growth intentions.

Identify specific personal growth and development intentions based on your self-awareness insights from this exercise. Write down actionable steps you can take to promote positive change and foster a deeper sense of self-awareness.

Example: I realize I could've prevented the situation by sending one simple SMS asking about our dinner plans. In the future, I'll be more proactive. Also, when I'm angry, I shouldn't be mean in my responses and ghost people. I should just be honest about what I feel, and if I don't feel like communicating, I should tell them that, too, so they understand me and give me space.

What are your personal growth intentions?

_____

_____

_____

_____

_____

_____

Worksheet 7: Self-Awareness Prompts

Following are a few self-awareness questions to ask yourself to encourage you to reflect and gain insight into your thoughts, emotions, behaviors, and overall self-perception.

Don't answer them all in one sitting. Choose one and dive into it. That is, select one and spend time utterly answering the question, letting your thoughts and answers take you where they want to go. As you go through these prompts, remember to be kind and patient with yourself.

1. How am I feeling right now, and what could be contributing to these emotions?

2. What thoughts have been foremost in my mind today, and how are they influencing my mood?

3. What moments today brought me the most joy, and why did they have such a positive impact on me?

4. What challenges did I encounter today, and how did I respond to them? Were there healthier ways I could have approached these challenges?

5. How did my interactions with others affect how I feel today? How did I contribute or influence the dynamics of each situation?

6. What activities or tasks do I engage in that bring me a sense of fulfillment and purpose, and how can I incorporate more of these activities into my life?

7. In what areas of my life do I feel the most confident, and how can I leverage this confidence in other aspects of my life?

8. What are my main priorities in life? Are my actions aligned with these priorities?

9. What aspects of my life do I find most challenging, and what steps can I take to overcome or adapt to them more positively?

10. How do I typically respond to stress or difficult situations, and are there healthier coping mechanisms I can adopt?

11. What are my long-term goals, and how can I break them down into smaller, achievable steps?

12. How do I prioritize self-care in my daily routine? What else can I do to nurture my well-being?

Radical Acceptance requires Self-Awareness
because you cannot accept reality AS IS if you don't see yourself AS IS.

Life doesn't just happen to us.
We play a role in what happens to us and unless we are fully aware of our participation in our reality, we cannot radically accept it.

Chapter 4. Non-Judgment: Breaking Free from the Chains of Criticism

One of the most difficult habits to unlearn is our tendency to judge everything—ourselves, others, song lyrics, TV shows, situations, the world, anything and everything. The irony is that most of us actually hate being judged. And when we're judged, we judge the other person as mean or unreasonable. See the irony there?

To be clear, passing judgment doesn't always mean appraising in the negative. You can judge someone as amazing, music as lovely, a film as groundbreaking, a book as inspiring, etc. So, to be non-judgmental is not about making zero judgments in life. To be non-judgmental is to develop the habit of NOT making negative assumptions. Because unless you know something to be true, accurate, or factual... you're just guessing.

Judgment = Opinion

Judgment = Assumption

Judgment ≠ Fact

Also, keep in mind that when we pass judgment, whether positively or negatively, we project aspects of ourselves onto whom or what we're judging. We judge based on that filter called "self." In doing so, we lose objectivity and become blind to the details and nuances of the object we're judging. In short, when we judge, we give others a glimpse of our inner selves.

So, why is it easy for us to judge? There are many reasons for our judgmental nature. Here are some of them:

Cognitive Bias. Cognitive (*mental*) bias (*prejudices*) is judging others based on our preferences, beliefs, or experiences. For example, suppose you're never late, and someone at work's a few minutes late for a meeting. Based on that single event, you may judge (label) your co-worker as "lazy." The issue with cognitive bias is that since we've established ourselves as the "judge" (based solely on OUR preferences), we don't apply the same criteria to our own person. If someone's late, they're lazy (*personality*). If you're late, it's the fault of traffic (*circumstances*).

Social Conditioning. Society and culture play a significant role in shaping beliefs and attitudes. We may adopt judgmental attitudes based on societal norms, stereotypes, or expectations.

Fear of "Different," "New," or the "Unknown." We may judge others because we're exposed to something unusual or different. Fear or discomfort with unfamiliar aspects of life can lead to judgmental attitudes.

Insecurity. Judgmental behavior can sometimes stem from low self-esteem or feelings of insecurity. Criticizing others may serve as a defense mechanism to deflect attention from our perceived shortcomings.

Lack of Empathy. We may be prone to judgmental behavior if we cannot understand others' perspectives or viewpoints. We cannot see their sides, so we'd rather judge them.

Need for Control. Judgment is a way to assert control or establish a sense of superiority. By labeling others as "less" or "wrong," we're, in effect, saying that we're "more" and "right." In this situation, passing judgment provides a temporary sense of power or validation.

Now, just because judgmental behavior is inherent to humans20,21, it doesn't mean you can't do anything about it. You can develop a non-judgmental behavior. But why should you want to?

For one, research shows that non-judgmental people tend to be happier.[22] That's not really surprising, is it? Imagine a state of being where you're not always calculating, assessing, or judging. That's a lot of stress avoided!

Also, non-judgmental people have better, more stable relationships because they're open to differences, capable of seeing others' points of view, and, as such, are more understanding and empathic. Wouldn't you want to have someone like this in your life? Someone who sees you for who you are and loves you as is?

Further, if you're non-judgmental, you lessen your own emotional suffering. Here's a simple example: imagine waking up and hearing rain outside your window. Your brain immediately judges the day as "dreadful." And that's it; you've set a tone of negativity throughout your day.

But what's the REALITY of the situation?
What's the one true FACT?
It's just raining.

So, **how do you cultivate a non-judgmental attitude?** Would it surprise you that mindfulness and self-awareness have much to do with it?

Mindfulness promotes **present-moment awareness**. And when your mind is preoccupied with NOW, you're less likely to dwell on past judgments or project them onto the future. If you do this one thing, you'll stop starting sentences with, *I "knew" you would...* or *I "knew" you were going to...* because sentences like that mean you're re-living something in the past and judging it to be applicable in the future.

Self-awareness helps you recognize patterns of judgment within yourself. By understanding these patterns, you can work towards breaking the habit of quick, automatic judgments. Using the same sample as above, the minute you start "reliving" something in the past, <u>Notice-Shift-Rewire</u> (page 29)!

In short, mindfulness and self-awareness promote a pause between stimulus and response. This mental pause allows you to respond to situations with greater thoughtfulness rather than reacting with snap judgments.

Another way to develop a non-judgmental behavior is to **challenge your assumptions**. When you notice yourself judging, ask yourself, *What else could be true? What can possibly be another reason for this?* Yes, argue with yourself! This is the fastest way to conclude that your judgment is based on an opinion or assumption, not facts.

Also, **develop empathy**. Put yourself in others' shoes and consider, even for a moment, *their* feelings and experiences. Mind you, you don't have to agree. You just have to understand their perspective.

Worksheet 8: What Else?

Judgmental behavior is often about being fixated on a *perceived* specific reason or outcome. However, as mentioned, until you know, you don't know for sure. This reflective exercise will help you develop the habit of giving others the benefit of the doubt.

Step 1. Identify a previous situation where you jumped to a conclusion and easily passed judgment on someone.

Example: I texted a friend to meet for drinks, but they weren't replying. Their "Read Receipt" notification is on, so I saw they read my message. Hours later, still no reply. So yeah, my mind went to several assumptions.

_____

_____

_____

_____

_____

_____

Step 2. What assumptions/judgments did you make?

Examples:

They're deliberately ignoring me.

They don't want to have drinks with me, and they're thinking how to say "no" nicely.

They're already out having drinks with our other friends and don't want me to know about it.

_____

_____

_____

_____

_____

_____

Step 3. WHAT ELSE was true?

Examples: My friend was giving an important presentation at a work meeting and didn't have time to reply to me.

_____

_____

_____

_____

_____

_____

Whenever you find yourself passing judgment, always ask, "*What else could be true?*" Do this often enough, and you'll cultivate non-judgmental behavior.

Worksheet 9: Empathic People Watching

When we people-watch, we tell ourselves we do so for entertainment, but truly, it's an opportunity to judge others. This exercise is designed to enhance your objective observational skills, foster empathy, and reduce the habit of automatically passing judgment. This activity encourages you to observe people in different situations with a curious and open mindset.

Step 1. Choose a public space like a park, cafe, or shopping mall where people engage in various activities. **Bring a notebook or journal** with you.

Step 2. Find a comfortable spot where you can observe people without feeling or being intrusive. Ensure you have a clear view of different interactions.

Step 3. Begin with a few minutes of **mindful breathing** to center yourself and cultivate present-moment awareness.

Step 4. Now, **watch people** without judgment. Notice their gestures, expressions, and interactions. **Resist forming any immediate opinions**.

Step 5. Be empathic. Put yourself in their shoes. Consider what might be going on in their lives, what emotions they might be feeling, and what their experiences could be like.

Step 6. Write down your observations. Describe only what you see. *Example: I notice a woman walking fast in front of me, a child in tow.*

Step 7. Is your mind making any immediate assumptions? If any judgments arise, write them without self-criticism. *Example: I think she's running late, so she's "dragging" her child.*

Step 8. Reflect. Explore where your assumptions came from. *Example: I lived with my father when I was a kid. Apart from work, he always brought me along, and we were always rushing. I was always being dragged somewhere.*

Step 9. Challenge your assumptions. What else could be true?
Example: WHAT ELSE could be true? Maybe the mom I saw wasn't rushing and was just walking fast. Also, now that I think about it, perhaps the child wasn't being dragged at all. The kid had shorter legs, so of course, they'd be walking slower and behind their mother.

Step 10. Move on to observe other people and different situations, repeating steps 4-9. Regular practice can enhance your ability to see the world from different perspectives and cultivate a more open, less judgmental mindset.

Identifying Self-Judgment and Self-Criticism

Although we hate being judged by others, we often judge ourselves and often in a negative light. This is because we've learned that to judge ourselves in the positive (e.g., *I'm looking great today. I'm so kind-hearted. I'm an excellent team leader.*) is being selfish and arrogant.

The problem with self-judgment is, again, we don't just state facts; we're criticizing ourselves. For example, we don't say *I don't know how to play the piano... yet*, we say, *I suck at playing the piano!*

Further, oddly enough, we *prefer* to judge ourselves. This way, we protect ourselves from the harsh judgment of others. Saying *I'm ugly* is less painful than hearing someone else say it. However, even though you think it's less painful, it's not less harmful. When we self-judge and self-criticize, we damage ourselves in so many ways.[23,24,25]

Harms Mental Health. Constant self-judgment contributes to negative thought patterns and can lead to conditions like anxiety and depression.

Lowers Self-Esteem. Excessive self-judgment erodes your self-esteem, making it difficult to appreciate your worth and accomplishments.

Limits Personal Growth. If you keep thinking you're incapable of doing something, chances are, you won't even try for fear of failing. This prevents you from exploring new things and evolving as a person.

Harms Relationships. Judging yourself harshly and constantly can impact your interactions with others, leading to strained relationships and difficulty forming connections. No one likes being around a "downer."

Increases Stress Levels. Constant negative inner chatter is draining! You're harsh on yourself; you blame yourself when things go wrong, even though the situation might be beyond your control, and you constantly second-guess yourself. This can lead to high levels of stress, anxiousness, and an overall decline in your physical health.

Undermines Resilience. You may struggle to bounce back from setbacks if you habitually judge yourself. Instead of thinking *I'll do better next time*, you might think, *Why bother?*

Impairs Decision-Making. A self-judgmental mindset may lead to indecisiveness because you constantly doubt your abilities.

Important: YOU deserve kindness and compassion—always. And there's absolutely nothing wrong with you extending these amazing, healing qualities to yourself. But to achieve this, you need to stop talking yourself down and start talking yourself up.

Silencing your inner critic requires mindfulness, self-awareness, and challenging your negative thoughts. For example, each time you think, " I look old, " take your cue from actress Anne Hathaway and say, "*Aging is just another word for living*." And instead of looking at your laugh lines, remember all the joyous moments that caused them, and keep smiling!

Here are other tips to put your inner critic into "Silent" mode.

- **Channel positivity** the minute you wake up. Say something like, "Today is a great day to have a great day!"
- **Acknowledge the good in you.** We all have good qualities, so feel free to write down anything and everything that makes you an amazing and

unique person. Now, don't overthink this. Examples: I'm good at singing. I'm organized in the bathroom. I care about my goldfish. (See also the Afformations worksheet below.)

- **Create a positive environment.** Surround yourself with energetic, happy people who see life as "half full," never "half empty." Avoid people and situations that bring you down. Establish and assert your boundaries so you're not "pulled" into anyone's drama.

- **Celebrate your achievements, no matter how small.** For example, "I cooked something I've never cooked before. That's being adventurous, baby. Booyah!"

- **Limit self-comparison.** Avoid constant comparison with others. Your journey is unique, and focusing on your life is more productive. If this entails a digital detox, then so be it!

- **Take care of your body.** A healthy body contributes to a healthy mind.[26,27] Eat and drink well, sleep adequately, and incorporate physical movement daily. This will make you feel and look good, boosting your self-esteem.

- **Practice gratitude.** Regularly reflect on the positive aspects of your life to counterbalance any negative thoughts. (See also The Underrated Power of Gratitude, page 132.)

- **Focus less on self-blame and more on solutions.** When things don't go as planned, make a mental jump from *What did I do wrong* to *How can I improve this situation*?

Worksheet 10: Afformations

You probably know positive affirmations already, so what are afformations? Introduced by mental health coach Noah St. John[28], afformations are positive questions you ask yourself.

The goal is to encourage your subconscious mind to find answers and solutions to questions, generating a positive and self-uplifting mindset. In simple terms, you engage your mind in diving deep into what you're good at and why.

Step 1. Ask yourself a positive question.

Examples:

What do I love about myself?

Why am I happy today?

What's the best thing that happened yesterday?

What do I like about my appearance?

What's your question?

_____

_____

_____

_____

_____

_____

Step 2. Engage your mind by writing down at least three positive answers you can think of answering your positive question.

Example:

Question: Why is my day filled with joy?

Answers:

a. I appreciate the small moments.

b. I surround myself with positive people.

c. I focus on what I can control.

Answer 1: _____

Answer 2: _____

Answer 3: _____

Answer 4: _____

Answer 5: _____

Step 3. Reflect. Take a moment to think about the answers. How do they make you feel? *Example: My answers made me feel grateful.*

_____

_____

_____

_____

_____

_____

Step 4. List down more positive questions related to your initial one.

Examples:

Original question: Why is my day filled with joy?

Related afformations:

- *What else can I do today to bring me joy?*
- *Why do I deserve this happiness I'm feeling?*

Related positive questions:

_____

_____

_____

_____

_____

_____

Step 5. Create a daily afformation practice. Repeat steps 1-4 every day for at least 30 consecutive days. Remember that the questions don't need to be earth-shattering. Simple questions such as "*Why is this cup of coffee/tea making me feel so good?*" are perfectly fine, too. The goal is to keep bringing positivity and good vibes into your life.

Radical Acceptance requires a Non-Judgmental attitude because if your mind is preoccupied with labeling yourself, people, things and situations as good, bad, right or wrong, you cannot accept them for simply what they are (as is).

Chapter 5. Embracing Imperfection

In life, we want to do our best. We're on our best behavior for our parents; we put our best efforts at school and at work; we present the best versions of ourselves when dating; we strive to provide what's best for our loved ones; we want to show up day in and day out as the best versions of ourselves.

This quest for "best" often means a pursuit of perfection. The problem is that perfection is a unicorn. It doesn't exist; it's a myth. So, if you live your life to impossibly high standards, you set yourself up for constant disappointment, causing yourself undue stress, burnout, anxiety, and depression.[29,30]

In contrast, embracing imperfection has been linked to greater happiness and better mental health.[31] So, how do you become okay with imperfection if you have a tendency for perfectionism?

Be mindful and live in NOW. Remember, what has happened has already happened. You cannot undo it.

Practice self-awareness. Tell yourself, *"This situation isn't ideal. That's okay. I don't need to react."* Next, **adopt a non-judgmental** attitude. *"This is no one's fault. No one desired this outcome. Now, how can I make this situation better?"*

Go for "flow" instead of perfect. "Flow" is a state of being totally absorbed and focused on something. You're engaging in an activity because of the joy it provides, not because of any desired result you expect. Focusing on "flow" enables you to enjoy the journey rather than being fixated on the destination.

Redefine "perfect." From now on, consider perfection a source of inspiration rather than a goal or established fact. Tell yourself that your goal is to do well, not to be flawless.

Celebrate "unique." Recognize and celebrate what makes you, others, or a situation unique. Keep in mind that if everything's the same, it becomes boring. Quirks and imperfections provide charm and individuality.

Choose freedom and authenticity. You don't need to follow the latest trend. You don't need to be loved by everyone. You don't need to accomplish the perfect project report every single time. You don't have to live up to anyone else's standards of beauty, success, or worth—and vice versa. Once you embrace imperfection, you embrace freedom, the freedom to be yourself.

Learn from undesired outcomes. Embracing imperfection doesn't mean you shouldn't aspire to be better. If things don't go as planned, don't dwell on mistakes or what went wrong. View the situation as a learning opportunity. What lessons can you glean from this? What should you avoid or continue to do in the future? How can this situation contribute to your personal growth?

Worksheet 11: Wabi-Sabi (侘寂)

Wabi-sabi is a Japanese concept that appreciates and finds beauty in impermanence (i.e., everything in life is fleeting) and imperfection. It's a perspective that values simplicity, asymmetry, and the authenticity of materials, so examples of wabi-sabi might be seeing the beauty in broken pottery, appreciating the aged look and ancient folds of an old love letter, etc.

Step 1. Embrace imperfection. Think of a recent situation where something didn't go as planned or was less than perfect. Describe how you initially felt about the imperfection.

Example: Last week, I baked a cake that didn't turn out as perfectly as I hoped. Initially, I was terribly disappointed; all that ingredients, time, and effort!

_____

_____

_____

_____

_____

_____

Reflect on whether you were able to find beauty or value in the imperfection over time.

Example: I did, actually. I thought I ruined the cake by accidentally adding cardamom instead of cinnamon, but the cake tasted great! As I was annoyed, I wasn't so careful with the icing anymore. Later, I found beauty in the imperfect swirls of the cake icing and considered it a unique creation.

_____

_____

_____

_____

_____

_____

Step 2. Reflect on the transience or fleetingness of life. Consider a moment or phase in your life that has changed or is changing.

Example: I'm reflecting on a past friendship. Though I'm no longer in touch with this person, I'm not bitter. I appreciate the beauty in the shared memories and the growth I've experienced with that friend.

_____

_____

_____

_____

_____

_____

Step 3. Look for simplicity and authenticity around you. Identify an object or aspect of your life that embodies simplicity and authenticity.

Example: I'm attached to this slightly worn-in book my sister gave me before I left for college. I find beauty in the simplicity of its well-read state, imagining how my sister enjoyed each page as I enjoyed going through them.

_____

_____

_____

_____

_____

_____

List at least three ways you can incorporate more simplicity in your daily life.

Example: de-clutter my bedroom, give away old gadgets, avoid toxic people

Way #1: _____

Way #2: _____

Way #3: _____

Step 4. Appreciate natural materials and flaws. Think about an item you own made from natural materials (wood, stone, etc.). Reflect on the beauty found in that item's natural flaws or imperfections.

Example: I have a small, old, wooden side table with visible knots, grain irregularities, and coffee stains. I love it!

_____

_____

_____

_____

_____

_____

Step 5. Look for asymmetry or irregularities in your environment. Look around your home and identify an area where asymmetry exists. Consider how this asymmetry adds character and interest to the space.

Example: My living room has plenty of mismatched sofa pillows. I used to be "bothered" by them. Now, I think they add "character" to my home.

_____

_____

_____

_____

_____

_____

_____

_____

_____

Wabi-sabi encourages us to find beauty in the imperfect, the fleeting, and what is natural (authentic, real). Practice this exercise often to cultivate a deeper sense of appreciation and contentment in your daily life.

Radical Acceptance requires Embracing Imperfection because you cannot accept reality AS IS if you expect it to be flawless or if you expect it to be anything at all.

Life is inherently flawed, and attempting to resist or deny imperfections leads to unnecessary suffering.

Chapter 6. Letting Go of Control

Emotional suffering usually stems from an inability to let go of control. I know a thing or two about this.

In my previous career as a Project Manager, I tended to micro-manage people. I found it extremely hard to delegate. I always followed up on everyone, and then I would shift to blaming when something went wrong.

I would blame myself, blame others, and I'd even blame fate if I had to. I would blame because I had an extremely difficult time accepting the situation. Emotionally, I was a wreck. I was always on my toes, vigilant of everything. This meant I was almost always stressed and anxious.

As a result, I developed the habit of pulling at my hair (*trichotillomania* or *trich*). It got so bad that I started sporting a very short haircut, telling everyone I preferred it because it meant less time to get ready in the morning. I also pulled, plucked, and tweezed my eyebrows until nothing was left to fix. (I could leave my home without any lipstick, but I couldn't without my eyebrow pencil.)

With Radical Acceptance, I've learned I had issues letting go because of my heightened sense of perfectionism, which was due to fear. I wanted things to be "perfect" because I was afraid of being found out that I wasn't good enough.

Here are some of the other reasons a person may be unwilling or unable to let go of control:

- **Fear of the unknown.** You're hesitant to try "new" because you're uncertain of what might happen. This indicates low self-esteem because you don't trust yourself outside your comfort zone.

- **Need for security.** You live a life of strict routines and planned approaches—designed by you. If the unknown or unexpected happens, your feelings of safety and security are challenged.

- **Perceived signs of weakness**. You may associate "letting go" with giving up or giving in. If you let go, you fear giving others the impression that you're "losing power," are not strong enough to see things through, or are incapable of defending your values and beliefs.

- **Past experiences**. Suppose you've experienced negative consequences as a result of you not having control (e.g., missing an important job interview because your ride was late picking you up). In that case, you might be unwilling to let go of control moving forward.

However, as mentioned above, the inability to let go heaps loads of emotional suffering. So, how do you free yourself from this self-imposed agony?

All the qualities we've discussed—mindfulness, self-awareness, non-judgmental attitude, and the ability to embrace imperfection—can help you let go of control.

You must also **learn to delegate**, but what does that mean? In my opinion, learning to delegate means learning to trust.

At work, it means trusting that your colleagues have the skills to contribute effectively to a project. In personal relationships, it involves trusting that your partner, friends, or family members are capable and willing to share responsibilities.

Ultimately, delegating involves recognizing that you don't have to carry everything on your shoulders. If you don't delegate, you deny others the opportunity to help and involuntarily convey that they are "incapable."

Please note that delegating (trusting) doesn't mean dictatorship. You're not supposed to give instructions but to let others participate in situations with you.

Another way to learn to let go of control is to **stop catastrophizing**, which is the belief that things will go terribly wrong if you're not in charge. So, what do you do? Shift from worst-case scenario thinking and start developing better stories in your head instead. For example, suppose your friends are coming over so you can cook dinner together. Your mind starts to race:

What's the menu? Are we just cooking whatever? Will that work?
What's the timing here? What if the meals are not done at the same time?
My kitchen will get all dirty. I'll have to stay up till 2 AM cleaning!

STOP! What's a better story here?

This is going to be fun. We're going to have a great time!
We need this. This is going to be great for our friendship.
I'm excited to eat something different tonight.

Here's another approach to help yourself let go of control: **develop your self-efficacy**, which is your belief in your ability to accomplish tasks, solve problems, or achieve goals. You see, the more uncertain a situation, the more we try to control it. Imagine all the angst we create for ourselves by trying to time to tame the uncertain or unknown! Instead, release that angst (need for control) and simply enjoy the experience, believing with all your heart and mind that whatever happens, you'll be able to deal with it.

But what about the stress and anxiety you feel inside when you're itching to control a situation? You shift your focus. Shift your mind from thinking about the situation to managing your stress and anxiety (i.e., manage your emotions). How? Firstly, do any of the mindfulness exercises under Chapter 2. Next, try the exercise on the following page.

Worksheet 12: Letting Go for Emotional Release

When you're trying to let go of control, you might experience unpleasant emotions. You might feel resentful, stressed, anxious, angry, etc. The following exercise will help you let go of control by helping you deal with the difficult emotions you might be experiencing as you attempt to release control.

Step 1. Label your emotions. Identify and label the emotions you are currently experiencing. Don't deny or ignore it.

Example: I'm extremely anxious. I'm not used to not being in charge.

_____

_____

_____

_____

_____

_____

Step 2. Accept your emotions. Remember, all your emotions are valid. You have a right to feel what you feel. Accept your emotion, but don't judge it.

Example: I'm anxious. This is what I'm feeling right now, and that's okay.

_____

_____

_____

_____

_____

_____

Step 3. Take a mindful breath. Breathe deeply a few times to relax yourself.

Step 4. Ground yourself. Engage your senses to ground yourself in the present moment. Look around you and identify five things you can see, four things you can touch, three things you can hear, two things you can smell, and one thing you can taste. (See also <u>Mindful Observation Using Your Five Senses</u>, page 27.)

Step 5. Body scan to let go of emotions. Did you know that emotions happen in the body?[32] Do a quick body scan (from head to toe) and pay attention to where you're feeling your emotions.

Example: I'm feeling my anxiousness on my shoulders. They're tense and bunched up.

_____

_____

_____

_____

_____

_____

Step 6. LET GO. Focus on the area of your body where you feel the emotion, take a slow and deep breath in, and imagine blowing away your emotion as you slowly exhale. (You can also say the word "Release" or "I release you" as you exhale.) Feel free to stretch, yawn, jump, etc., if you feel like it too.

Do this exercise each time you feel yourself resisting your efforts at letting go of control. It may seem difficult initially, but with constant practice, you'll find yourself going through less emotional distress as you surrender control of situations.

Forgiveness: Letting Go of Control Over Your Emotions

What does forgiveness have to do with surrendering control? In many respects, the difficulty to forgive reflects an inability to let go of control over emotions.

When you struggle to release feelings of anger, hate, jealousy, resentment, bitterness, sadness, etc., you are, in a sense, trying to control those emotions by choosing to hold on to them instead of allowing the natural emotional process to unfold (i.e., acknowledging feelings, accepting them, and then consciously choosing not to let them dictate your well-being).

For example, suppose your partner cheated. You're furious, and you break up. Time has passed, but you're still angry and don't want to forgive them. However, by being unwilling to forgive, you're holding onto your anger and hate. You're choosing to stay in emotional misery and negativity because you cannot let go of control over these emotions.

You might be thinking, *but they don't deserve my forgiveness!* This is where most of us get it wrong. (I know I did.) Forgiveness is, first and foremost, for the benefit of the forgiver (you), not the one being forgiven. By forgiving, you're choosing to let go of unpleasant and unhealthy emotions and energy (negativity) and deciding not to carry it forward with you anymore.

Think of it this way: if you feel bitterness and keep bitterness in your heart, you become a bitter person. But if you feel bitterness and choose to let it go, you can become happy.

Further—and here's something I really had to dig deep for—if you're not willing to forgive, ask yourself what trauma or damage the person or situation triggered in you? Going back to our cheating example, if you cannot forgive them, it's perhaps because you've always had abandonment issues. And rather than accept that you may have low self-esteem or a fear of loneliness, you'd rather stay angry with your ex. After all, "mad" is easier, less painful, and safer than "sad."

So, if you really think about it, to be unforgiving is to be in denial.

I will not forgive you. I will stay angry because this is your fault.
(Translation: I will not forgive you. I will stay angry because I don't want to deal with feeling abandoned and undesired.)

Important: Forgiving is NOT forgetting, denying, approving, excusing, or condoning. Forgiving is not letting the accountable "off the hook." It's releasing yourself from the hook of emotional negativity and suffering.

While discussing forgiveness with my Radical Acceptance group, someone asked, "*If forgiveness is for me. Can I forgive and not let the other person know?*" I believe you can, especially if you don't want to have any further contact or maintain any form of relationship with them.

We always associate forgiveness with the person who hurt us. I ask you to reframe your idea of forgiveness as a personal, internal, and self-healing process that primarily benefits your emotional well-being. As such, you can forgive privately, focusing on your own peace of mind and emotional release. However, if you believe communicating your forgiveness would bring closure or positively impact your relationship with the other person moving forward, you may choose to do so at your discretion.

If forgiving others is good for you, imagine the healing you accomplish when you forgive yourself.

Unfortunately, for many, forgiving oneself is harder than forgiving others.[33] For one, there are more difficult emotions involved. Research shows that while *anger* is the only significant predictor of unforgiveness, *anxiety, guilt, shame,* and *anger* are associated with self-forgiveness.[34]

Let's flip our example and suppose that you cheated on your partner. Difficulty forgiving yourself may be due to your enormous guilt and shame over what you did. You might be angry at yourself for the situation you caused, and you might feel anxious about your future, not knowing if your relationship will survive the cheating.

Self-forgiveness may also be difficult if you keep thinking about *what could have been* or all the *what-ifs*. This rumination reinforces feelings of guilt and shame and, as such, strengthens any belief you may have that you are "bad."

Judging yourself too harshly or significantly overestimating your responsibility in the situation (i.e., *I take full responsibility. It's all on me.*), as well as believing that you brought this all on yourself (i.e., *I'm weak. I have low morals. I would've cheated sooner or later.*) are also reasons why self-forgiveness may be difficult.

Notice that all the above reasons point to the same thing: You're not letting go of control over your emotions. You're choosing to stay negative instead of allowing the natural emotional process of forgiving yourself to unfold. With self-forgiveness, this natural process means (1) taking responsibility for your actions, (2) exhibiting genuine remorse, (3) sincerely apologizing and making amends, and (4) learning from your mistakes. (See <u>Worksheet 13: The 4 R's of Self-Forgiveness</u>, page 86.)

Forgiveness, whether directed to others or yourself, is, for all intents and purposes, acceptance of pain. Something horrible happened, and you're feeling a host of negative emotions. However, staying in that negative state doesn't do anyone any good. To feel better, release yourself from emotional suffering, and heal... you must learn to forgive.

Worksheet 13: Forgiving Others

Step 1. Reflect on the hurt. Take a moment to reflect on the specific actions or behaviors of the person you must forgive. Write down how these actions have affected you emotionally and any residual feelings of resentment or anger.

Example: I asked my best friend of 20 years to help me find a temporary place near them as I had to be there for three months for work. The place was great, but I later learned I was paying 50% more on rent. My "best friend" was pocketing the money. No, I didn't know they took it upon themselves to take a "fee." When I arrived, I even treated them to dinner to say thanks, and they never said anything. I've developed trust issues. I even started to question myself. Like, wow, I don't know how to pick friends?

_____

_____

_____

_____

_____

_____

Step 2. Acknowledge your emotions.

Acknowledge and identify the emotions that have arisen due to the hurt you have experienced. Write down the specific feelings you are experiencing, such as anger, betrayal, or sadness, without judgment.

Examples: I feel angry, dismayed, betrayed, and used.

_____

_____

_____

_____

_____

_____

Step 3. Practice empathy. Try to understand the perspective of the person who hurt you. Write down any possible reasons or circumstances that may have influenced their actions, fostering a sense of empathy and understanding.

Example: What would drive a person to take money from a friend? I guess if they had debts or health problems for which they need money.

_____

_____

_____

_____

_____

_____

Step 4. Release your resentment. Challenge any lingering feelings of resentment or grudges you may be holding onto. Write down affirming statements that help you release these negative emotions and open yourself up to the possibility of forgiveness and emotional liberation.

Example: I won't stay angry with you anymore. I won't let anger take the better of me. I'm releasing any feelings of betrayal. I won't let this incident completely prevent me from enjoying my other friendships.

_____

_____

_____

_____

_____

Step 5. Write a forgiveness letter. This is optional, but it might help to compose a forgiveness letter addressed to the person who hurt you. Express your feelings honestly and openly, emphasizing your willingness to let go of the pain and move forward with compassion and understanding. Remember, you don't have to send this. This is for you.

Example forgiveness letter to a toxic family member:

I've been reflecting on our relationship, and I find myself carrying a lot of hurt and disappointment. It's not easy to admit, but holding onto these negative emotions is taking a toll on my well-being.

For my own peace of mind, I'm choosing to forgive you for the past. Forgiveness doesn't mean forgetting or condoning hurtful actions, but rather releasing the hold these memories have on my heart.

I'm not sure if I'm going to send you this letter. For now, it's more of a personal reflection; about freeing myself from the weight of resentment.

I hope, in time, we can both find our paths to healing and perhaps even rebuild our relationship. For now, I'm taking steps to focus on my own growth and well-being.

_____

_____

_____

_____

_____

_____

Step 6. Visualize the act of forgiveness. Engage in a visualization exercise where you imagine yourself letting go of the hurt and offering forgiveness to the person who has wronged you. For example, imagine releasing a forgiveness balloon, and as the balloon flies away from you, imagine any unpleasant emotions leaving your body. (If you want, skip visualizing and carry out the act.)

Step 7. Set boundaries for self-protection. Establish healthy boundaries to protect yourself from potential harm in the future. Write down specific actions you can take to set boundaries that prioritize your emotional well-being and prevent similar hurtful experiences from occurring again.

Example: I'll avoid putting myself in a situation involving friends and money. If I ever need help from a friend again that requires money, I'll make sure I verify amounts or pre-discuss with them if there are fees or anything of the kind involved. Honesty and directness will prevent headaches and heartaches later.

_____

_____

_____

_____

_____

_____

Step 8. Embrace your emotional liberation! After forgiving, give yourself some time to get used to it. Afterward, celebrate your journey toward emotional liberation and forgiveness. Write down how forgiving others has contributed to your personal growth, resilience, and capacity for empathy and understanding.

Example: These past weeks, I feel "lighter," as if a burden has been lifted off my shoulders. I also feel that I can enjoy my current friends better; I'm not always on guard or second-guessing their intentions.

_____

_____

_____

_____

_____

_____

Worksheet 14: The 4 R's of Self-Forgiveness

Genuine self-forgiveness is an active process; i.e., there are steps involved. It's not just saying, "*Oh, people make mistakes. I'm human, so I forgive myself.*"

In fact, saying or believing this might indicate a lack of self-awareness over any wrongdoings you may have done. It may also be a sign that you're unwilling to let go of control over your emotions. That is, you're glossing over the issue instead of accepting and addressing it. The following exercise aims to help you attain true self-forgiveness.

Step 1. Responsibility

Take responsibility for your actions. Think of a situation where you made a mistake or did something you regret. Describe the situation briefly.

Example: I made a hasty decision at work without considering the potential consequences. As a result, extra man-hours had to be put in, and the project deadline was not met. The client got mad and left us a bad review online.

_____

_____

_____

_____

_____

_____

Step 2. Remorse

Explore and identify the emotions associated with your actions.

Example: I feel guilty and embarrassed. I was rushing. I should've taken the time to think things through. If I did, the project might not have had issues and finished on time.

_____

_____

_____

_____

_____

_____

Allow yourself to experience and express these emotions fully. Remember, this is not *wanting* to feel further guilt or shame about your mistake. It's allowing your emotions to go through its natural course.

Step 3. Restitution

Consider *practical steps* to make amends or restitution. List actions you can take to repair the harm caused, and then create a plan for implementing these actions.

Example:

   (1) Gather the team for a meeting and apologize sincerely.
   (2) Mention that I'm aware of the negative consequences of my actions.

_____

_____

_____

_____

_____

Step 4. Renewal

What have you learned from the situation? Identify areas for personal growth and positive change. Set specific goals for self-improvement and commit to them.

Example: I've learned that rushing important decisions is never a good idea. I need to take my time and be more thorough. I also learned that I should always remember that it's not just me involved in a project. My decisions affect other people, so I shouldn't take them lightly.

_____

_____

_____

_____

_____

_____

Radical Acceptance requires Letting Go of Control because you cannot accept your present reality AS IS if you're trying to shape it and bend it to your will.

Forgiveness of others and self is necessary because emotional negativity hinders your ability to embrace the present moment with all its pain and imperfections.

Chapter 7. Radical Willingness

Everything we've discussed so far is meaningless if you're not willing; willing to see reality for what it is, and willing to modify any thoughts, feelings, or habits that are not working for you.

You might think, "*Ava, shouldn't you have mentioned willingness at the start?*" Truthfully, I believe that unwillingness or resistance often comes in the form of *denial*. That is, you may not be seeing or realizing that you're unwilling and, as a result, end your journey before you even start.

However, if you're mindful (*present in the moment*), self-aware (*capable of objectively seeing yourself*), nonjudgmental (*not applying any negative assumptions or opinions*), capable of embracing imperfection (*understanding that healing is not a linear process*), and are okay with letting go of control (*able to trust the process*), then, dear reader, NOW you can be radically willing to accept Radical Acceptance.

Please keep in mind that to experience *unwillingness* is normal. In the context of emotional healing, willingness is the ability to feel emotions without instantly escaping or avoiding them. And dealing with emotions—accepting them, feeling them, and understanding their WHY— can be difficult and painful. So we are unwilling. Unwillingness keeps us "safe."

In the context of life in general, willingness is the ability to openly and actively engage with experiences, challenges, and changes—without resistance. It means being open to what happens, going with the flow of life, and taking in both the good and bad things with an open heart and mind.

Being willing means being ready to learn, change, and grow, knowing that every moment brings new lessons and chances to improve yourself.

Now, as with previous qualities discussed in this book, willingness doesn't mean denying, approving, wanting, or condoning. For example, suppose you're feeling intense grief due to the loss of a loved one. Willingness is not being "okay" with their death. It's about being willing to feel and experience your grief. Why? To feel better. Willingness to feel grief transforms grief into pain you can endure.

Worksheet 15: Willing Hands

As mentioned, we feel emotions in our bodies. **Willing Hands** is a body-focused exercise often applied in DBT.1 By physically fostering a sense of openness, we can slowly manage our resistance against painful or unpleasant emotions of experiences.

So, don't tense up or ball your hands into tight fists the next time you're in an unpleasant situation and feeling intense emotions (e.g., anger, hatred, shame, guilt, etc.). Instead, deliberately **open your hands, keep your palms up, and relax your fingers**.

If you're still feeling resistance, open your hands slowly–opening or stretching one finger at a time. Next, stretch your hands wide open, fingers apart (almost tensing), and then slowly relax them to a *willing hands* position (relaxed, but open)

Tip: Feel free to combine **Willing Hands** with any mindfulness exercise, such as Counting Breath Practice (page 24) or Mindful Deep Belly Breathing (page 25).

Remember, you're not fighting your emotions or denying them. You're willing to experience them so you can get through them.

Worksheet 16: The Willingness Experience

Often, unwillingness is a sign of fear: fear of the unknown, fear of losing control, fear of being exposed, fear of looking like an idiot, fear of being uncomfortable, etc.

This exercise will help you overcome your fear using a concept called *imaginal exposure*. By imagining how an event will play out, you'll prepare yourself for any eventualities and thus be willing enough to go through the actual experience.

Step 1. What are you resisting? Identify an event (or specific areas in your life) where you have felt resistance or reluctance to engage fully.

Example: A BIG party at work is coming up, and every fiber of my being is unwilling to attend.

_____

_____

_____

_____

_____

_____

Step 2. Why are you unwilling? Reflect on the reasons behind your resistance, acknowledging any fears or uncertainties holding you back.

Example: I'm NOT a conversationalist. I feel very uncomfortable surrounded by people I don't know.

_____

_____

_____

_____

_____

_____

Step 3. Imagine the event. Find a quiet and comfortable space where you will not be disturbed. Sit or lie down. Imagine the event you are dreading as if it were happening right in front of you right now.

Important:

    (1) Don't just imagine your role in the event. Imagine other people, who they are, where they are, and what they say.

    (2) As you imagine the event unfolding in your mind, you might feel resistance or even physical signs of tension and stress. At this stage, label what you're feeling without judgment.
       Example: I'm feeling uncomfortable and anxious.

       _____

       _____

       _____

    (3) Next, mindfully take a deep breath and do <u>Willing Hands</u> (page 91).

    (4) Slowly embrace a mindset of curiosity and openness. Do the following:

    Put your left hand over your heart.
    Put your right hand over your left hand.
    Breathe in deeply.
    As you breathe out, say this out loud: "I am willing to feel this feeling of _____, in just this moment. It's okay. This is natural. It's part of the process."

If you feel your resistance is fading, you can proceed to the next step. If not, repeat items (2) to (4).

Step 4. Address the reason for your unwillingness. Reflect on your answer in Step 2 above. Now that you're more open and willing, you can move from the problem to the solution.

Example: I'm not a conversationalist. What can I do:
> *(a) Pre-think topics to discuss in advance.*
> *(b) Bring a +1, so I'm not alone.*
> *(c) I'll just actively listen! Instead of focusing on what I need to SAY, I'll genuinely listen and ask open-ended questions to keep the conversation going.*

_____

_____

_____

_____

_____

Radical Acceptance requires Radical Willingness because you cannot accept reality AS IS if you're not fully open and committed to embracing it.

Radical Willingness encourages you to release resistance, let go of the need for things to be different, and actively engage in the present moment.

Chapter 8. Radical Self-Acceptance

We all like looking at ourselves in the mirror, but we rarely look beyond what's skin-deep or superficial. Actually, if you think about it, what does the very act of looking in the mirror make us do? We notice everything that needs to be fixed.

Messy hairs need to be combed and put in place, acne needs to be covered up, fine lines need to be erased, and on and on it goes until everything is... *enhanced*. (This is not to say that you shouldn't want to present yourself in a good light. I'm just highlighting how our mind unconsciously shifts to "fix" when we look at ourselves.)

Some of us avoid getting to know ourselves; we fear what we might discover. (*What if the very characteristics we proclaim we don't like (e.g., lying, cheating, close-mindedness, etc.) are the very ones we possess?*) Others, however, already have an idea but refuse to accept it. (*Me? Low self-esteem? Nah, I just don't like putting myself out there, you know?*) Others still are just clueless. (*I don't know why I'm always being passed for promotions!*)

Radical self-acceptance is complete and unwavering unhiding. It means fully and completely accepting yourself just as you are. It's like saying, "*I'm okay, just as I am, with all my strengths and weaknesses.*" Instead of being hard on yourself for not being perfect, you embrace yourself with kindness and understanding. It's a deep and unconditional love for yourself.

However, radical self-acceptance doesn't mean condonement. You shouldn't use it as an excuse for not addressing problematic behavior. (*I'm a chronic liar. That's just who I am. I accept that.*)

It also doesn't mean complacency. It means that you acknowledge that you're a work in progress. You're capable of change; you're capable of learning, healing, growing, and evolving.

For me, at the start of my healing journey, I radically accepted myself as "broken." I was in a state of utter unhappiness. I was experiencing deep internal turmoil, and I didn't know why. Still, I accepted that THAT was my current self. But it didn't mean that I had to stay that way. However, please note that radical self-acceptance doesn't mean you always need to "level up." I suck at anything mathematical, mechanical, or technical, and that's okay. I don't need to learn to be better in those aspects. I'm a capable person even without those particular skills.

So, radical self-acceptance is seeing ALL your strengths and weaknesses. And the only aspects that require change are the ones that hinder your happiness and personal well-being.

Unwavering self-acceptance also means the willingness to see yourself as you are in difficult situations. For example, you and your partner had a big argument. You can't contain your anger and throw a glass against a wall. Your partner is shocked into silence and walks out the door. In the following silence, you replay the argument, and because you're capable of self-awareness, you can see certain points during the fight that contributed to its escalation.

My timing's off. I shouldn't have started this discussion the minute my partner arrived home.
Hmmm, I was the one who raised my voice first.
Throwing the glass against the wall wasn't my best moment.

And now you acknowledge your emotions:

I'm feeling frustrated, angry, and sad. I'm also ashamed for throwing that glass.

Next, you address your emotions:

I feel tightness in my chest over what happened.

What do you do? Address it with mindful breathing.

I'm feeling resistance, a resistance to reconcile and make peace.

What do you do? Address with Willing Hands or practice Walking Meditation. And as you do, visualize the benefits of making peace.

Next, take responsibility for your participation in the situation—without regret, criticism, or judgment.

I participated in that fight. My thoughts, feelings, words, and actions helped escalate it.

Practice radical self-acceptance:

I acknowledge my emotions and reactions during the argument. I'm not going to criticize myself or judge myself because this argument doesn't define me; it's a moment in a much larger journey. I do acknowledge the need to make amends. When my partner arrives home and the timing's right, we'll revisit the topic more positively and healthily.

So, **how do you foster radical self-acceptance**?

Firstly, unwaveringly tune into yourself. **Mindfulness** and **self-awareness** are keys to getting to know and accepting yourself for who you are. (See also Focusing, page 100.)

Genuine **self-forgiveness** is also a form of self-acceptance because you're not just saying words (*I forgive myself*) but going through an active process.

Self-compassion is another way to radically accept yourself. It's probably the most important thing you should be extending to yourself, but hardly ever do. Why? Because we're our worst critics. If a friend messes up, you'll likely say, "*Hey, you got this! It's all good.*" If you find yourself in the same situation, you'll probably mentally beat yourself up about it—over and over.

However, being harsh or overly critical of your weaknesses or shortcomings doesn't benefit you because you're subconsciously telling yourself you're not "good." (The lack of self-compassion stresses the negative self-impression.) Instead, acknowledge your less-than-amazing qualities and, if it makes you happier or advances your well-being, find ways to change or improve on them.

Self-compassion also entails acknowledging your pain and giving yourself empathy, understanding, and support.

Examples:
I'm doing my best, and that's all I can ask of myself.
I may feel alone, but I'm not alone. I can choose to reach out for help and support.
I don't need to rush my anger/pain/grief/disappointment. I have a right to feel them and go through them.
I regret not always attending my kids' school activities, but it doesn't make me a bad parent.

I mentioned before that I had this habit: if I tripped, dropped something, or forgot something, I'd silently say, "*Dumb Ava!*" I don't do that anymore.

Cultivating a nonjudgmental behavior towards myself and self-compassion have completely removed that unhealthy habit.

One of the most amazing aspects of accepting yourself is finding yourself in a scenario where you truly want to learn more! *What more could I do? How can I experience even more happiness and fulfillment? How else can I make a positive impact on the world?*

One way to do this is to **nurture curiosity about yourself** and your inner world. You must be okay with going out of your comfort zone to do this. After all, you cannot discover anything new or different about yourself if you're always doing the same thing. So, ask yourself, *What interesting activities and experiences do I want to try?*

Examples: swimming, baking, taking a weekend vacation with a new friend, sitting alone in a coffee shop to enjoy my own company, hosting a 5-course dinner, etc.

New experience #1: _____

New experience #2: _____

New experience #3: _____

New experience #4: _____

New experience #5: _____

Worksheet 17: Focusing

Focusing is an exercise developed by psychologist Eugene Gendlin.[35] It's similar to mindfulness but involves a more narrowed focus on bodily sensations or the "felt sense." The idea is that by unwaveringly focusing on these sensations, you create a non-judgmental space to explore your feelings, encouraging an attitude of curiosity and acceptance.

Step 1. Find a quiet and comfortable space where you won't be disturbed. Take a few deep breaths to center yourself and create a sense of calm.

Step 2. Choose a topic to explore. Identify a specific issue or situation that you want to explore. It could be a challenge, decision, or something that feels unresolved.

Step 3. Initiate awareness. Close your eyes if comfortable and bring your attention inward. Ask yourself, *What am I feeling about this issue right now?* Allow any emotions or sensations to surface without judgment.

Step 4. Locate the felt sense. Pay attention to your body. Where in your body do you feel the intensity or sensation related to this issue? It might be a tightness, warmth, or other feeling. Notice the nuances of this felt sense.

Step 5. Describe the felt sense. Using words, describe the felt sense as precisely as possible. What does it feel like? Is it heavy, light, contracted, expansive? Give it a name or label it if that feels natural.

Step 6. Check for a positive shift. After describing the felt sense, check for any subtle shift or release. Sometimes, simply acknowledging and describing the felt sense can bring positive change.

Step 7. Continue exploring. If the issue still feels unresolved, ask yourself, *"What else is there?"* and repeat the process. Be patient and open to whatever arises.

Step 8. Express gratitude. After focusing, thank yourself for taking the time to explore your inner experience. Acknowledge any insights or shifts, no matter how small.

Step 9. Reflect. Take a moment to reflect on what you've discovered. Consider how this exploration might inform your understanding of the issue or guide your next steps.

Focusing is a gentle and intuitive process, and there's no right or wrong way to experience it. Trust your inner wisdom and allow the process to unfold naturally. And whatever you discover about yourself, remember to be kind and accepting.

Worksheet 18: Self-Compassion Break

Struggling with something? Use this worksheet to guide yourself through a self-compassion break whenever you face challenges or feel overwhelmed.

Step 1. Practice mindful awareness.

What are you going through? Take a moment to acknowledge your current thoughts and feelings. Notice and name the suffering.

Examples:

I'm really struggling in my marriage right now.

I'm drowning at work.

I'm hurting.

_____

_____

_____

_____

_____

_____

Step 2. Establish common humanity.

Recognize that difficulties and challenges are a natural part of the human experience. You're not alone in this world facing struggles. At this very moment, someone is having similar experiences. Check which statement relates to you now, or write your own statement:

[ ] *We all struggle at various points in life.*

[ ] *This experience is just part of being human.*

[ ] *Living includes ups AND downs.*

[ ] *Now that I think about it, what I'm going through will be hard for anyone.*

[ ] *I'm not the only one suffering in this situation. My _____ is likely feeling the same.*

[ ] *I'm not the only one grieving.*

[ ] *We all encounter struggles and moments of self-doubt.*

[ ] _____

Step 3. Self-kindness.

Offer yourself kindness and understanding. Imagine what you would say to a friend going through a similar situation. Speak to yourself with the same warmth and compassion.

Examples:

I'm struggling, but it doesn't mean I'm giving in. I know I have it in me to make this better.

I give myself kindness. I give myself unconditional love.

I am here for myself.

I made a mistake, but I know in my heart. I'm a good person.

_____

_____

_____

_____

_____

_____

Step 4. Reflect. How do you feel now? Take a moment to reflect on any shifts in your thoughts or feelings after completing your self-compassion break. Notice if there's a greater sense of understanding and acceptance.

Example: I feel better. Just being quiet for a while and giving myself attention has improved my spirits.

_____

_____

_____

_____

_____

_____

Radical Acceptance requires Radical Self-Acceptance
because you cannot accept reality AS IS if you're not capable of
acknowledging your worth, strengths, and imperfections—without
judgment.

Radical Self-Acceptance is the foundation
on which Radical Acceptance stands and builds.

Part III: Navigating Life's Challenges with Radical Acceptance

"Challenges are what make life interesting, and overcoming them is what makes life meaningful." – Joshua J. Marine

Radical Acceptance is *actual reality* acceptance. You see, what you consider as "real" might be your *perceived reality* of what is.

Perceived reality is how you see or believe things to be, while actual reality is how things truly are, independent of personal interpretation. Your thoughts, emotions, and past experiences influence perceived reality. In contrast, actual reality is the objective, factual state of things. It's like wearing glasses; what you see might be influenced by the color of your lenses, but the actual reality remains the same for everyone.

It's hard to shift from perceived to actual reality because of all our conscious and unconscious resistance to what is. Part II: Bringing Acceptance Into Your Life encapsulates all the habits you need to unlearn and all the qualities you need to put in its stead to see and accept actual reality.

Keep in mind that Radical Acceptance is acknowledging reality without putting energy into trying to change it. You might be thinking, *How's that possible? If my current situation (reality) is difficult, painful, or unpleasant, shouldn't I want to change it?* Of course, you should! However, remember that reality is the sum of the past.

For example, suppose you're entering the kitchen with an armful of laundry. You didn't see that your kid's birthday cake has been delivered and is on the kitchen counter. You accidentally knock it over, and now the amazing and expensive birthday cake is on the floor.

What's Radical Acceptance here? The birthday cake is on the floor.

You cannot rewind the previous minutes; ergo, it's pointless and unhelpful not to accept the reality of the situation. It will just bring up negative or unpleasant emotions, which do nothing to remedy the situation.

So, you accept and focus on your next steps to ensure a better outcome. In this example, that might mean cleaning the mess and calling someone to purchase and bring a new cake. In less than an hour, you experience another reality: a great birthday party for your kid.

Chapter 9. Handling Difficult Emotions

Emotions are what make us human. Our capacity to feel a wide spectrum of emotions, from joy and love to sadness and anger, adds depth and richness to our human experience. While some emotions are difficult to experience, they still uniquely shape our understanding of ourselves and how we experience life. Consider the example of grief.

Grieving the loss of a loved one is an emotionally challenging experience. It brings intense sadness, loneliness, emptiness, and sometimes even anger. While these emotions are undoubtedly difficult to go through, they play a crucial role in shaping our understanding of ourselves and the complexity of human connections.

Grieving allows us to confront the depth of our emotions, reflect on the significance of the relationship we had, and ultimately help us navigate the process of healing and finding meaning in life despite the loss. So, even though the emotions associated with grief are challenging, the *grieving process* contributes to a richer and more profound understanding of our own emotional landscape and the intricate fabric of human experience.

Note that the whole grieving process (initial pain/loss -> reflection on the significance/beauty of the relationship -> acceptance or peace with the loss -> healing and moving on with life)[1] is an example of letting the natural process of healing unfold. If you don't radically accept grief, if you hold on to that pain, the pain turns to emotional suffering.

---

[1] Please note that this is just an example. The grieving process is different for everyone.

CONTENT WARNING: *The following may be distressing or triggering. Be mindful and take a break when necessary. If you feel overwhelmed, please don't hesitate to ask for assistance or consult a specialist.*

Please choose a difficult emotion you may be feeling now or experience frequently in your life.

Shame	Inadequacy	Anxiousness / Anxiety
Guilt	Self-Doubt	Grief
Low Self-Esteem	Regret	Unworthiness
Anger	Jealousy	Fear
Other:		

Next, please radically accept the emotion. Place your hands over your heart and say it out loud or just to yourself. For example, *I feel crippled by shame.*

_____

_____

_____

_____

_____

_____

Take a deep and mindful breath and ask yourself, *Why am I feeling this?* Who or what's triggering this emotion right now? For example, *I've been molested as a child. I mentioned this to a friend, but they didn't believe me. Today, that same "friend" has reached out on FB. It's brought out many buried feelings in me.*

_____

_____

_____

_____

_____

_____

If you sense negative self-judgments, challenge them with more balanced and compassionate perspectives. For example, _That situation was not my fault. I believe me. I'm more than that experience._

_____

_____

_____

_____

_____

_____

Pay attention to your body. Where are you feeling the negative emotion? Breathe deeply into it and release it. If possible, express your feelings in a constructive, releasing way. For example, if you're feeling grief, give yourself a moment to have a big, loud cry. If you're angry, do something physical, such as going out for a vigorous walk or run. If you're feeling shame, write a letter of self-forgiveness.

What do you want to do?

_____

_____

_____

_____

_____

_____

After radically accepting your emotions, visualize yourself feeling lighter as you release yourself from emotional suffering. Note that you may need to do this more than once and use other techniques (e.g., Mindful Observation Using Your Five Senses (page 27), Self-Compassion Break (page 102), etc.), and that's 100% okay. Radically accepting and dealing with difficult emotions is a process that should not be rushed.

Coping with Change and Uncertainty

Time is always moving forward. Life is constantly changing. And so, recognizing the nature of change and uncertainty is crucial for cultivating Radical Acceptance. Please keep the following in mind:

- **Impermanence.** Change is the only constant in life. Everything, including emotions, relationships, and circumstances, is subject to change. So, open your hands and embrace impermanence instead of trying to grip or hold onto now. Radically accept NOW, but happily welcome NEXT.

- **Unpredictability**. The future is inherently unpredictable. Unforeseen events and circumstances can shape your journey no matter how well you plan. Acknowledging the unpredictability of life fosters resilience and openness to new possibilities.

- **Unknown**. Uncertainty often brings with it the unknown. However, instead of fearing it, Radical Acceptance encourages curiosity and openness. It's thinking that every unknown moment carries the potential for growth and transformation.

- **Adaptability.** Resisting change can only lead to suffering. Why fight the reality that day ends into night, and night gives way to day? Radical Acceptance encourages adapting to change with an open heart. It involves finding the balance between acknowledging the pain of change and recognizing the opportunities it presents.

- **Growth**. Change and uncertainty provide fertile ground for learning and personal growth. Each challenge, setback, or unexpected turn holds valuable lessons. Radical Acceptance involves seeing these experiences as opportunities for development.

Change is an inevitable aspect of life. Radically Accept that reality, and you'll find yourself capable of fully enjoying the richness of the present.

Chapter 10. Building Wonderful Relationships

Your Relationship as a Safe Space

We want this in a healthy, loving, and stable relationship: safety. We don't want to be judged, blamed, scrutinized, or disregarded. To cultivate this safety and security, you and your partner must radically accept each other. If you can't, then the relationship is a disservice to you both because neither of you will ever truly be fulfilled. On the other hand, if you radically accept each other, flaws and all, then you have a relationship you can both consider your sanctuary. For example:

Partner: *I messed up. I was rushing and got a speed ticket.*

Instead of: *Of course you did! (judgment) And how much is that ticket?! (guilt-tripping)*

Say this: *What? Babe, are you okay? You good?*

In this example, nonjudgment and empathy win the day. Imagine the effect this has on your relationship. Imagine how this scenario creates a culture of safety and security where you and your partner can express yourselves authentically and without reservation.

Everyone Is Always Doing their Best

Radical Acceptance in a relationship also means adopting the mindset that **everyone is always doing their best**.

Now, you might be thinking, *No, they're not! If my partner did their best, they wouldn't have gotten a speeding ticket.*

In this example, though, what you're really hopping mad about is the outcome of their intentions. You're angry about the *result* of what happened, not the intent behind their actions. For example, you're pissed about your partner getting a speeding ticket. But what if they drove too fast because they intended to get home to you sooner?

Granted, your partner's best intentions may not always result in the best outcome. (*That speeding ticket is really expensive!*) Still, just like you, they're incapable of predicting the future. So, instead of jumping into an argument about an outcome (*what happened*), try instead to understand their intentions (*what they were trying to do*).

Examples:
Outcome (what happened): Someone dropped and broke an expensive vase.
Possible intention (i.e., what they tried to do): House clean.

Outcome: Someone's late for dinner.
Possible intention: They tried to finish off work to be free with you this weekend.

Accusations = Fears

Often, in the heat of the moment, we might throw out accusations and take it upon ourselves to label our partner's thoughts or emotions.

You just don't love me anymore, do you!
It's ok; admit it. You think our relationship sucks.
I know my weight is bothering you.

However, when you accuse, you're really projecting your own fears.

You just don't love me anymore, do you!
(I'm afraid you don't love me anymore)

It's ok; admit it. You think our relationship sucks.
(I'm afraid I'm losing you.)

I know my weight is bothering you.
 (I'm bothered by my weight, and I'm scared it's affecting us.)

Now, consider what happens when someone is accused. They get *defensive*, right?

You: *You just don't love me anymore, do you?*
Partner: *Huh? Where did THAT come from?!*

So, to prevent this escalation, don't accuse. Radically accept your own emotions and fears and own up to them.

Not: *You just don't love me anymore, do you!*
But: *I feel insecure in our relationship. I'm afraid you don't love me anymore.*

What if your partner is the one who's accusing you? Don't get defensive; see through the statement and reassure their fears.

Hear: *You just don't love me anymore, do you!*
Practice mindfulness...
Say: *Babe, of course, I love you. We're just arguing, and arguments are temporary. This fight has nothing to do with our love for each other. Come here; we're good.*

At this stage, I'd like to repeat that Radical Acceptance is never about approving, denying, ignoring, excusing, or condoning bad or unhealthful behavior—including relationships.

For example, suppose you discovered that your partner secretly withdrew funds from your account to purchase something you never discussed. In this case, practice Radical Acceptance by acknowledging your emotions about the situation and then pausing before reacting.

Also, reflect on your assumptions or expectations about shared finances. Perhaps you and your partner have different beliefs about how money is spent in your relationship to begin with.

Next, apply Radical Acceptance principles toward your partner by adopting a nonjudgmental attitude while discussing the situation. Extend empathy and jointly focus on finding solutions rather than dwelling on the problem. The following is a personal example:

Here's a pet peeve I have with my husband—he forgets. I'm not talking about things like forgetting to take out the trash. We discuss something important, he agrees, and he forgets.

I openly communicated my frustration and told him that when these incidents happen, I struggle with trust. (Notice that I said *"I" struggle with trust*, which is me taking responsibility for my own feelings. If I had said, *Why do YOU always forget?!*, it would be a blaming and judgmental attitude.) How do I know whether he will remember to do something or not? I don't want to second-guess him. So, what do we do? How can we help each other?

My husband suggested noting things on his mobile phone because jotting them down will help him remember them more. And we agreed that if that didn't help, we'd use the BIG whiteboard in his home office. Luckily, we didn't reach that option.

Does this mean he never forgets? He never forgets the really important stuff. I've radically accepted that he will occasionally forget some things or points, and that's okay. I embrace his imperfection because he so readily embraces mine.

The above tips also apply to every relationship in your life, not just intimate ones. For example, say you have a co-worker who consistently takes credit for your ideas during team meetings, undermining your contributions and causing extreme frustration.

In this scenario, radically accept the situation, acknowledge your emotions, and pause before reacting. Next, initiate a private conversation with your co-worker, openly communicating how their actions made you feel. Seek understanding, extend empathy, and then shift the focus of the conversation to finding solutions. For example, state that you would like your co-worker to amend their previous comment and give you credit in the next meeting, attribute the idea to you in a Minutes of the Meeting memo, etc.

Radical Acceptance in relationships also often means establishing and asserting boundaries. Remember, you're part of your reality. You have influence over what happens next, which may mean being clearer and more assertive about your boundaries.

Examples:

No. I don't want to go to your parent's house every Sunday. I'd like us to spend time alone together, or at least I don't want to be forced to come along if I don't want to.

No. I don't appreciate others taking credit for my ideas. Please don't do it again. I WILL speak up immediately the next time that happens.

Hey, bestie, you know I'm here for you, but I can't be your emotional punching bag today. I have problems of my own I need to address right now.

Dealing with Conflict

Despite your and your partner's best efforts, there's conflict between you. That's okay; that's inherent in all relationships. So, how do you accept and address it? Practice **mindful interactions**.

Practice active listening. During discussions with your partner, listen to understand, not to argue. Make it your goal to understand *their* perspective. Think of it this way: you share equal responsibility in your situation. Understanding their 50% enables you to see the whole picture.

Emphatic speaking. When discussing, show empathy by validating your partner's viewpoints. This indicates that you truly heard them, so they'll be more open to hearing you. For example, *I understand you're mad at me for not calling that I won't be home for dinner.*

Speak only from your perspective. When communicating, use "I" statements. Remember, you're sharing *your* perspective.

Examples:

~~You always leave me alone.~~ I feel ignored.

~~You don't spend time with me.~~ I want more time with you.

~~You don't care!~~ I feel sad because I feel like my feelings are being ignored.

~~You don't pick up after yourself.~~ I get stressed when I see clothes scattered on the floor.

I'm Sorry

We've discussed the healing power of forgiveness, but equally, healing is the ability to genuinely apologize and say I'm sorry.[36]

Radical Acceptance has healed me so much that I'm sometimes surprised by all my other changes. I used to have difficulty saying, "I'm sorry." I used to think it was the same as saying "I failed" or admitting I was "less" in any way. But then I learned that being unable to apologize is the perfect example of *avoidant behavior*, which is denying or escaping difficult thoughts, emotions, and situations. Saying sorry made me feel uncomfortable and vulnerable, so instead of owning up to my mistakes, I'd rather just be nasty or find something (or someone) else to blame.

Acceptance is the complete opposite of avoidance, so by fostering Radical Acceptance into my life, I sort of just woke up one day unafraid of saying, "I'm sorry," and those two little words can be oh-so healing for relationships!

For one, saying "I'm sorry" **shows that you're aware of your actions and how they affect your partner**. Unwillingness to apologize is like saying "Hmpf!" to your partner's feelings. In contrast, apologizing shows that you care about your partner's feelings and are ready to try to make things right.

Usually, we don't want to apologize to our partners because we're admitting guilt. If we apologize first, they won't take responsibility for their part in the fight. In truth, our partners just want to hear "*I'm sorry*" for hurting them. So you see, this has nothing to do with guilt or who's at fault. Saying sorry because you're part of an event that caused your partner pain means you care about their feelings. This, in turn, will help your partner feel safe with you and in your relationship.

Saying sorry also **helps rebuild trust and connection**. If your partner feels hurt or betrayed, saying sorry can help validate their feelings and show that you understand and care about them. This can make talking and healing easier, strengthening your connection in the long run.

Further, apologizing **helps avoid future arguments** by admitting you made a mistake and promising to do differently next time.

Relationships are vital to the human experience[37]. Yet, we often find ourselves in conflict with loved ones and get stuck in issues rather than finding ways to improve our connections. Radical Acceptance helps us remove that "*It's complicated*" label we often place on our relationships by fostering understanding, empathy, and open communication. For me, Radical Acceptance is what helped make my relationship a "safe space."

Worksheet 19: Repair and Rebuild Using Radical Acceptance

If your relationship is in a dark place, try this exercise. It will help you acknowledge and embrace the reality of the situation, promoting understanding and providing a foundation for making conscious efforts to move forward.

Step 1. Practice radical self-acceptance.

Begin by practicing Radical Self-Acceptance. Reflect on your feelings, thoughts, and actions related to the relationship. Acceptance of yourself lays the groundwork for accepting others.

Step 2. Acknowledge reality.

Face the current state of your relationship without denial or judgment. Acknowledge the challenges, conflicts, and emotions involved. This step is crucial for understanding what needs to be addressed.

Step 3. Practice mindful awareness.

Take a moment to experience present-moment awareness. Give yourself the freedom to feel your emotions without reservation or judgment. This will help you be mindful and self-aware during conversations and interactions with your partner.

Step 4. Foster open communication.

Initiate open and honest communication. Express your thoughts and feelings calmly, using "I" statements to avoid blame. Encourage the other person to share their perspective without judgment or interruption.

Step 5. Practice active listening.

Practice active listening to truly understand the other person's experiences and emotions. Validate their feelings, even if you don't agree with them. This builds a foundation of empathy.

Step 6. Cultivate empathy and compassion.

Cultivate empathy and compassion for the other person's struggles and challenges. Recognizing that everyone makes mistakes and understanding each other's vulnerabilities is important for healing.

Step 7. Let go of any resentment.

Release resentment and grudges. Radical Acceptance involves letting go of negative emotions tied to past events. Forgiveness, not forgetting, is a powerful tool for moving forward.

Step 8. Set clear and healthy boundaries.

Establish clear and healthy boundaries to prevent recurring issues. Clearly communicate your needs and expectations, and encourage the other person to do the same.

Step 9. Problem-solve together.

Approach challenges as opportunities for collaborative problem-solving. Work together to find solutions that will benefit you both, fostering a sense of teamwork and shared responsibility.

Step 10. Commit to change.

Demonstrate a genuine commitment to positive change. Take concrete actions to address the issues discussed. Consistent effort and a willingness to learn from mistakes are key elements to rebuilding trust.

Step 11. Celebrate progress!

Acknowledge and celebrate progress in the relationship. Recognize positive changes and express gratitude for efforts made by both parties. This reinforces a positive cycle of growth.

Step 12. Seek professional support (if needed).

If your relationship is deeply strained, consider seeking professional support, such as couples therapy or counseling. A neutral third party can provide guidance and facilitate constructive communication.

Repairing relationships with Radical Acceptance is a transformative process that will help you move beyond past hurts and build a stronger, more resilient connection. However, it requires patience, empathy, and a shared commitment to growth. Be kind and forgiving of each other, and don't let setbacks deter you from trying and trying and trying again.

Practicing Radical Acceptance as a Parent

Do you have children? And if so, do you find your parent-child relationship being tested a few too many times? Radical Acceptance can help.

Here's an example situation and how Radical Acceptance can help you as a parent: Your 15-year-old teen came home extremely intoxicated.

Mindfulness.

Accept reality AS IS. Your underage child came home drunk. The situation is not ideal, but it has already happened. You cannot change it. Take a mental pause to let this situation sink in. You have every right to feel your emotions, but you don't have to act on them. Create space between stimulus (situation) and response (your next steps).

Self-awareness.

What are you thinking? What are you feeling? What do you want to say or do? Whatever it is, just be aware of them. See if you're succumbing to any patterns of behavior that are not helpful.

For example, do you want to scold your child? Is this an automatic response (pattern) you have? That is, if your child does something unpleasant -> scold them!

If this is a pattern, is it helpful? Has it ever done any good in the past? What would scolding accomplish *now* when your child is already intoxicated?

Ask yourself if this situation is triggering something in you? Do you have any previous negative experiences or traumas related to alcohol (e.g., a father who came home drunk too often and became abusive)? If so, check that your initial response is not a knee-jerk reaction to your past and, as such, has nothing to do with your child today.

Non-judgment.

Refrain from making unfounded conjectures. Check any biases you may have (e.g., *This is the influence of their new friend at school!*). Also, avoid making sweeping assumptions (e.g., *Oh, now it begins!*). Remember, unless you know for sure, you're just guessing.

Embracing imperfection.

Accept that your child is not perfect (human), has made a mistake, and will continue to make their own mistakes. This is how they'll learn.

Letting go of control.

Let go of the need to control your child's life, even if you believe it's for their own good. This is ONE mistake from which they can learn. There's no need to step in and take over. (Besides, that will just build resentment.)

Radical willingness.

Be willing to accept the effects of this situation on you—and process it.

This is making me afraid that this is not a one-time thing. But, wait, that's not being fair to my child or me.

Be willing to learn from this situation.

I've learned drinking is a trigger.

Be willing to listen and truly hear your child when discussing the matter.

Radical self-acceptance.

This situation doesn't mean you're a bad parent. If you see any shortcomings on your part, practice self-compassion and work on that shortcoming moving forward.

Alright, you've radically accepted the situation and put yourself in the right and helpful frame of mind to discuss what happened with your child. Remember to actively listen, understand their why, be emphatic, and work together to avoid a repeat of the incident. Here's an example:

Parent: Hey, can we talk for a moment?

Teen: Sure, what's up?

Parent: When you came home last night, I could tell you've had a bit to drink. How are you feeling?

Teen: I'm okay, just had some fun with friends.

Parent: I get it; socializing is a part of growing up. But I'm concerned and want you to know that my concern comes from a place of care, okay? I remember being your age, and I understand the desire to experiment.

Teen: Yeah, it was just a party. Everyone drinks nowadays.

Parent: I hear you. Parties can be fun, but they can also have consequences. I'm not here to lecture or blame. I want us to have an open conversation. What made you decide to drink last night?

Teen: I don't know, everyone was doing it, and I thought it would be cool.

Parent: It's natural to want to fit in. I appreciate your honesty. Let's talk about how we can make sure you're making choices that align with your values and keep you safe. What are your thoughts on that?

Teen: I guess I should be more careful next time.

Parent: That's a good insight. It's good to be aware of the choices we make and their potential impact. If you ever find yourself in a situation where you're uncomfortable, I want you to feel you can reach out to me anytime. I promise: no blaming, no judgment. Okay?

Teen: Yeah, okay.

Parent: Well, that's it then. Now, go do your homework! Love you, bud.

In this example, a *consequence* may be necessary (e.g., removing phone privileges for a week, being grounded, etc.). It's your right to impose that as a parent, but ensure your child understands why you're doing it. New boundaries may need to be set, too. Again, discuss and involve your child in the process. This way, they'll be more likely to accept rather than oppose.

Part IV: Living a Life of Radical Acceptance

"Healing is an inside job." - Dr. B.J. Palmer

Chapter 11. Authenticity: You "As Is"

As you embrace Radical Acceptance, you'll find that authenticity follows. As you peel off your mask and strip off layers upon layers of frustrations and expectations, what you're left with is you—as is.

Authenticity can be scary. To be real is to be raw and vulnerable because we share our weaknesses and struggles, too. Authenticity is even uncommon nowadays because social media has rewired our brains to believe and seek the unreal.[38,39]

So, why even seek it? Why be authentic? Because the alternative—to be fake—is exhausting! This is what started my journey. I was so tired and drained from pretending that I suffered a burnout and a breakdown. So, I'll take authenticity and peace anytime.

Everything about Radical Acceptance screams authenticity, so by this page in the book, dear reader, I believe you've already started to slowly meet the real you. Here are some more tips to cultivate authenticity in your life:

Self-reflection. Take time to reflect on your values, beliefs, and aspirations. Understand what truly matters to you and align your choices with your authentic self.

Embrace vulnerability. Be open and honest about your thoughts and feelings, even if it makes you feel vulnerable. Vulnerability fosters genuine connections and allows others to see the real you.

Know your boundaries. Set and communicate clear boundaries that respect your values and well-being. Think of it this way: If you say "Yes," even when you really don't want to, you're not being truthful to yourself and your values.

Express your creativity. Engage in activities that allow you to display your creativity and individuality. Whether it's through art, writing, or other outlets. Find ways to showcase your unique perspective.

Accept your flaws. Embrace your imperfections as integral parts of who you are. Nobody is perfect, and acknowledging your imperfections can lead to greater self-acceptance.

Authentic communication. Be true to your thoughts and feelings in your communication with others. Avoid pretending or conforming to societal expectations if it contradicts your authentic self.

Build authentic relationships. Surround yourself with people who appreciate you for who you are, not how you benefit them. Cultivate relationships where you feel accepted and supported in expressing your true self.

Tip: Focus on building your offline relationships. I find face-to-face interactions and physical presence provide a deeper sense of connectedness. If you have online relationships that do the same for you, great! But don't let it prevent you from exploring offline relationships, too.

Live your values. Identify your core values and strive to live in alignment with them. Your actions and decisions should reflect the principles that matter most to you.

Authenticity is a continual process of self-discovery and self-expression. As life unfolds and you learn and grow, you will change. Embrace who you become, too!

Chapter 12. Cultivating Gratitude and Joy

Cultivating gratitude and joy is important for Radical Acceptance because it shifts your focus from what's lacking or negative to what is positive and present in your life.

Looking back, it amazes me how I lived in fear without realizing it. Afraid I'm not good enough; afraid I have a depression disorder; afraid of being alone; afraid of not being seen; afraid of being too seen; afraid of being idle; afraid of doing too much... on and on it went.

In being afraid of *what could be*, I never enjoyed *what is*. Radical Acceptance changed all that. Today, joy and gratitude define me.

Finding Joy in The Present Moment

People usually interchange joy and happiness, but there's a slight difference. Joy is a state of being (an attitude); happiness is an emotional response to something external.

For example, you wake up, and there's this underlying sense of contentment, fulfillment, and even excitement that exists. That's joy. You go down and see that your partner has been up for a while and has breakfast ready for you. A big smile spreads over your face. That's happiness.

Finding joy in the present moment is about appreciating and fully experiencing NOW. It's like experiencing happiness 24/7 and in HD. It involves letting go of worries about the past or the future and immersing yourself in the current experience.

Mindfulness is key to finding joy in the present moment. Usually, our default setting is "rushed," and we're breathing, thinking, feeling, and acting in "next." But in so doing, we miss everything in "now." Sad, right?

By doing the opposite, by deliberately being fully present in the moment, you can discover joy in simple moments and activities. Whether it's savoring the taste of your favorite food, enjoying a beautiful sunset, or relishing a quiet moment of solitude, finding joy in the present enhances your overall well-being and deepens your connection to life.

I like to think of it this way: finding joy in the present moment is like collecting shells of happiness, resilience, positivity, and all the good stuff. When something unpleasant happens, the situation no longer affects me as much as it used to. Why? What's a pebble of annoyance compared to my jars and jars of collected joy? Here are some tips to cultivate happiness and joy in your life:

1. **Smile often.** If smiling feels unnatural try starting with small, genuine smiles in front of a mirror. Practice until it becomes a more natural and comfortable expression. Remember, even a subtle smile can positively impact your mood and how others perceive you.

2. **Practice mindfulness.** It will help slow you down and focus, and you'll be amazed at all the beautiful things you never truly noticed before.

3. **Get in "flow"** (page 65). Engage in activities that give you peace and happiness.

4. **Connect with others.** Build your relationships. Here's a tip: What can my friend/partner/colleague/family member do to make me happy right now? And then do that for them.

5. **Take care of your health.** Physical well-being is closely linked to emotional well-being. Ensure you get enough sleep, eat nourishing food, and exercise regularly.

6. **Learn and grow.** When you're in a good place, you think you want to stay there forever, but really, you don't because it becomes boring, stagnant, fixed. What you should be focused on is learning and growing. "New" engages the mind, and it's crucial for happiness.[40,41]

7. **Practice self-care!** Why do we always take care of ourselves last? Self-care is crucial for finding joy because it involves *intentional actions* prioritizing our well-being and overall happiness. (See the bonus section, 51 Self-Care Activities, page 144.)

8. **Practice acts of kindness.** Whether big or small, performing acts of kindness for others boosts your happiness![42]

9. **Stay away from "toxic."** Identify and minimize exposure to negative influences, whether in the form of people, places, situations, news, or other media. Surround yourself with positivity!

10. See tip #1.

The Underrated Power of Gratitude

Gratitude is when you feel thankful and appreciative for the good things in your life. It's about recognizing and being glad for the positive experiences, people, or moments that bring you happiness or make a positive impact.

Humans are funny creatures. We want to be happy but focus on what makes us miserable. We often say we want things to be simpler and then complicate our lives.

Cultivating an attitude of gratitude will help you rewire your brain to focus on the good because it enables you to count blessings instead of burdens. It truly has the power to alter your perception of the world.

According to research, gratitude comprises two phases: seeing goodness in one's life (recognition) and giving credit to the external sources of that goodness (acknowledgment).[43]

Phase 1: Recognition. This is when you notice and understand the good things you have in your life. For example, you realize you have a friend who always supports you or remember a time when someone was kind to you.

Phase 2: Acknowledgment. After recognizing the good things, you actively say thank you or appreciate them. For example, you tell your friend how much their support means to you or write a note to express gratitude for someone's kindness.

So, gratitude is not just *Oh, I'm happy for* _____. It's a dynamic process involving intentionally acknowledging and appreciating those benefits. It's like, first, you see the sun shining (recognition), and then you say, "Wow, the sun makes everything brighter, and I'm grateful for that" (acknowledgment and appreciation).

Here are some ways to help you develop an attitude of gratitude in your life. Why don't you put a checkmark on the first three you want to do?

___ **Mindful Moments.**
- Take a few moments each day to appreciate your surroundings.
- Notice the beauty in simple things, like a blooming flower or a clear sky.

___ **Express Gratitude Verbally.**
- Tell the people around you that you appreciate them.
- Say "thank you" sincerely and often.

___ **Random Acts of Kindness.**
- Perform small acts of kindness for others without expecting anything in return. It could be as simple as holding the door open or helping someone with a task.

___ **Gratitude Walks.**
- Take a walk and consciously think about things you're grateful for. Connect your steps with positive thoughts.

___ **Gratitude Jar.**
- Write down moments of gratitude on small notes. Place them in a jar and read them whenever you need a boost.

___ **Reflect on Challenges.**
- Consider the lessons and growth that come from difficult experiences.

- Find something positive even in challenging situations.

___ **Connect with Nature.**

- Spend time outdoors; appreciate nature. Feel gratitude for the Earth's beauty and the life it sustains.

___ **Volunteer Work.**

- Engage in volunteer activities to help those in need. Witnessing the impact of your efforts can be profoundly gratifying.

Gratitude is about consciously focusing on the positive aspects of life, big or small. It's a mindset that can be developed through regular practice and awareness. So, keep at it!

Worksheet 20: Gratitude Journaling

Are you new to gratitude journaling? Here are some prompts to help you get started. Feel free to customize this worksheet to suit your preferences and add additional sections if needed.

Instructions:

1. **Set aside time**. Find a quiet and comfortable place to sit.
2. **Reflect on your day**. Think about the positive aspects of your day.
3. **Express gratitude**. Write down things you're thankful for in the spaces provided.
4. **Be specific**. Include details about each item you list.
5. **Feel the gratitude**. As you write, focus on the emotions associated with each gratitude entry.
6. **Rinse and repeat.** Make gratitude journaling a regular part of your routine.

Date: Today's Date _____

Step 1. Indicate a person or relationship. Write the name or describe a person or a relationship you are grateful for today. Why are you thankful for this person or relationship? Describe specific actions or qualities.

Example: I'm grateful for my husband. He woke up earlier than me, gave me a kiss, and told me he'd wait for me downstairs for breakfast.

_____
_____
_____
_____

_____

_____

Step 2. Identify an experience or achievement. Describe a positive experience or achievement from today. What made this experience special, and how did it contribute to your day?

Example: I got further with my writing project than I thought. I'm grateful for the sense of achievement I feel.

_____

_____

_____

_____

_____

_____

Step 3. Focus on nature or the environment. Reflect on something in nature or your environment that you appreciate. What about this natural element or environment brings you a sense of gratitude?

Example: I appreciate the small wooded area near our home. I'm grateful I can step out and take a refreshing and invigorating walk anytime I want.

_____

_____

_____

_____

_____

_____

Step 4. An act of kindness. Recall an act of kindness that touched you, either given or received. How did this act of kindness impact your day or your perspective?

Example: I always smile and greet people with "Good day" when I'm out for my walks. I think this simple act of kindness has the power to brighten someone's day.

_____

_____

_____

_____

_____

_____

Step 5. Something about yourself. Identify a personal quality or trait within yourself that you are grateful for. How does this quality positively influence your life or the lives of others?

Example: I'm loyal and faithful. I'm grateful for this quality because it's a great foundation for my relationships. This loyalty creates a sense of trust and security for those around me. Although sometimes my loyalty leads me to put others' needs before mine, I appreciate the deep connections it fosters and the strength it adds to the bonds I share with loved ones.

_____

_____

_____

_____

_____

_____

Step 6. Note a surprise or blessing. Note any surprises or blessings that brought you joy today or recently. What made these surprises or blessings stand out to you?

Example: My best friend baked some cookies and brought me some "just because!" It made me very happy, and knowing they think of me felt great.

_____

_____

_____

_____

_____

_____

Take a moment to reflect on the overall feelings of gratitude during today's journaling session. Note the positive feelings that come from being grateful, and let them stay with you throughout your day.

Conclusion

"Healing may not be so much about getting better as about letting go of everything that isn't you – all of the expectations, all of the beliefs – and becoming who you are."
– Rachel Naomi Remen

Radical Acceptance can bring so much transformation, healing, and joy into your life—if you accept it. Here's a quick recap.

In Part 1: Understanding Radical Acceptance, we discussed the concept of Radical Acceptance, what it is, and what it's not. There are so many misconceptions about "acceptance." We often link it to agreement, approval, giving in, trivializing, etc. This chapter explains why this is not the case and demonstrates the true meaning of acceptance and its benefits for your life.

In Part 2: Bringing Acceptance Into Your Life, we dive deep into the eight aspects of Radical Acceptance. These are the keys that open the doors of this concept into your life.

- **Mindfulness** is the ability to live in now and simply "be."
- **Self-awareness** is the ability to observe and understand yourself completely and without judgment.
- **Non-judgment** is the skill to resist jumping to negative assumptions. It's the ability to stop guessing and predicting, and developing the skill of always looking for facts.

- **Embracing imperfection** is the art of being perfectly okay with what's NOT perfectly okay.
- **Letting go of control** is the ability to free yourself from any fear of the unknown. It's learning to trust others and yourself.
- **Radical willingness** is the ability to openly and actively engage with experiences, challenges, and changes—without resistance.
- **Radical self-acceptance** is loving yourself—as is.

In Part 3: Navigating Life's Challenges with Radical Acceptance, you learned how Radical Acceptance can be applied to every unpleasant situation or difficulty you find yourself in life. You can use it to handle negative and crippling emotions and apply its principles to improve your relationships.

In Part 4: Living a Life of Radical Acceptance, you discovered how to keep Radical Acceptance a permanent fixture in your life. By shedding your mask, breaking down your walls, being authentic, finding joy in every moment, and cultivating gratitude, you'll find that being a radical accepter is not so hard after all.

As you go through your journey, please always take a moment to track your progress or just to check in with yourself. That, in itself, is important for your self-discovery and growth. (If you need help with this, see Bonus: Radical Acceptance Self-Reflection.)

In my life, Radical Acceptance has been one of the most beautiful and freeing concepts I've ever come across. Each day of learning and applying it meant more weight off my shoulders and less emotional suffering. I hope it's as healing for you as it has been for me.

Bonus: 51 Self-Care Activities

Self-care is essential and personal. Here's a list of 51 simple and rejuvenating options at your fingertips. Each day, try to choose at least one that resonates with you and brings you joy and relaxation.

[ ] **Take a Bubble Bath**: Create a relaxing atmosphere with candles and calming music.

[ ] **Read a Book**: Escape into a good story or explore a topic of interest.

[ ] **Practice Deep Breathing**: Focus on your breath to reduce stress and increase mindfulness.

[ ] **Go for a Walk**: Enjoy nature and get some fresh air.

[ ] **Try Meditation**: Practice mindfulness to calm your mind.

[ ] **Listen to Music**: Create a playlist of your fav feel-good tunes.

[ ] **Journal**: Write down your thoughts and feelings.

[ ] **Unplug**: Take a break from your digital devices.

[ ] **Do Yoga**: Stretch and strengthen your body.

[ ] **Cook a Healthy Meal**: Nourish yourself with good food.

[ ] **Get a Massage**: Relieve tension and relax your muscles.

[ ] **Practice Gratitude**: Reflect on the positive aspects of your life.

[ ] **Have a Picnic**: Enjoy a meal outdoors.

[ ] **Watch a Movie or TV Show**: Have a movie night.

[ ] **Draw or Paint**: Express your creativity on paper or canvas.

[ ] **Take a Nap**: Recharge with a short nap.

[ ] **Visit a Museum**: Explore art and culture.

[ ] **Learn Something New**: Take up a new hobby or skill.

[ ] **Connect with a Friend**: Spend quality time with someone you care about.

[ ] **Visit a Park**: Enjoy green spaces and nature.

[ ] **Plan a Staycation**: Relax at home as if you were on vacation.

[ ] **Dance**: Move your body to your favorite music.

[ ] **Attend a Yoga Class**: Join a class for guided practice.

[ ] **Practice Mindful Eating**: savor each bite.

[ ] **Declutter Your Space**: Create an organized and calming environment.

[ ] **Do a Puzzle**: Challenge your mind with a crossword or jigsaw puzzle.

[ ] **Write Affirmations**: Affirm positive statements about yourself.

[ ] **Go to a Spa**: Treat yourself to a spa day or spa treatments at home.

[ ] **Volunteer**: Give back to your community.

[ ] **Watch the Sunrise or Sunset**: Connect with the beauty of nature.

[ ] **Visit a Farmer's Market**: Explore fresh and local produce.

[ ] **Create a Vision Board**: Visualize your goals and aspirations.

[ ] **Try Aromatherapy**: Use essential oils to create a soothing atmosphere.

[ ] **Go Stargazing**: Enjoy the night sky.

[ ] **Take a Photography Walk**: Capture interesting sights on camera.

[ ] **Attend a Workshop or Class**: Learn something new in a group setting.

[ ] **Do a Digital Detox**: Disconnect from screens for a day.

[ ] **Play a Musical Instrument**: Make music for relaxation.

[ ] **Practice Random Acts of Kindness**: Spread positivity to others.

[ ] **Visit a Botanical Garden**: Surround yourself with beautiful plants.

[ ] **Plan a DIY Spa Day**: Pamper yourself with skincare and relaxation.

[ ] **Practice Tai Chi**: Experience the flowing movements for relaxation.

[ ] **Write a Letter to Yourself**: Reflect on your achievements and goals.

[ ] **Visit a Beach**: Listen to the sound of waves and enjoy the sea breeze.

[ ] **Take a Photography Walk**: Capture interesting sights on camera.

[ ] **Coloring**: Engage in adult coloring books for a creative outlet.

[ ] **Play a Sport**: Engage in physical activity you enjoy.

[ ] **Plan a Digital Detox Day**: Take a break from screens and technology.

[ ] **Do a DIY Project**: Channel your creativity into a craft.

[ ] **Enjoy a Comedy Show**: Laughing is a great stress reliever.

[ ] **Visit a Library**: Explore new books or find a cozy reading spot.

Bonus: Radical Acceptance Self-Reflection

Reflecting on your Radical Acceptance progress is crucial to self-discovery and growth. Take a moment to consider the following aspects:

Mindfulness Practice.

- Reflect on your mindfulness practice.
- Have you integrated mindfulness in your daily life? What do you do? How has it influenced your perspective?

Awareness of Thoughts.

- Reflect on how your thought patterns have evolved since embracing Radical Acceptance.
- Have you become more aware of negative self-talk? Are you better at redirecting those thoughts?

Handling Emotions.

- Evaluate how you manage your emotions now compared to before.
- Are you more capable of acknowledging and accepting your emotions without judgment?

Relationship Dynamics.

- Consider the impact of Radical Acceptance on your relationships.
- Have you noticed changes in how you interact with others? Are your connections healthier?

Self-Compassion.

- Assess your level of self-compassion.

- Are you kinder to yourself in challenging situations? How has this affected your overall well-being?

Response to Challenges.
- Think about how you respond to life's challenges.
- Have you developed a more balanced and resilient approach? How do you navigate setbacks?

Gratitude and Joy.
- Explore the presence of gratitude and joy in your life.
- How often do you consciously acknowledge and appreciate positive moments?

Areas for Further Growth.
- Identify areas where you still encounter difficulties in acceptance.
- What aspects of Radical Acceptance are most challenging, and how do you plan to work on them?

Remember, the journey of Radical Acceptance is ongoing. Celebrate your progress, and use your reflections to guide continued growth and development. Each step forward is a testament to your commitment to a more authentic and fulfilling life.

A Little Help?

Hello there! I wrote this book especially for you, and I hope you enjoyed it and found it helpful.

Many people don't realize how hard it is to get reviews and how much they help us authors. So I'd be incredibly grateful if you could take just a few seconds to write a short review about this book on Amazon, even if it's just a few words. Every single review makes a difference, so I appreciate your help!

How to Leave a Review
Just visit https://life-zen.com/rad-review or scan the QR code on this page to leave a quick review directly on Amazon. Thank you!

What's Next?

Want to get a free copy of our upcoming books?
Just join our **LifeZen Book Club** to get early access to new releases.
https://life-zen.com/book-club

Audiobook

Enjoyed This Book?
Listen to the Audiobook Version!

If you loved reading this book, why not take the experience to the next level?

With the **Radical Acceptance Workbook** audiobook, you can immerse yourself in the story wherever you are – whether you're driving or relaxing at home. **Narrated by Annete Martin**, the audiobook brings radical acceptance to life in a way you've never experienced before!

Why Choose the Audiobook?
- **Convenience**: Listen while multitasking or on the go.
- **Engagement**: Hear the words brought to life through dynamic narration.
- **Flexibility**: Switch seamlessly between reading and listening with most audiobook apps.
- **Great for Auditory Learners!** If you find that you absorb information better by listening rather than reading, this audiobook is perfect for you.

Get Your Copy Today!
The audiobook version is available on Audible here: https://amzn.to/4g2SzDm or scan the QR code on this page.

Thank you for being a reader, and I hope you enjoy the audio journey just as much!

Radical Acceptance Workbook
Audiobook on Audible

Further Reading

The ACT Therapy Workbook for Adults

An Easy-to-Read (No Jargon!) Acceptance & Commitment Therapy Guide for Mindfulness and Mental Wellness

If you're ready to deepen your self-acceptance and personal growth journey, this book is the perfect next step. It offers powerful exercises and strategies rooted in Acceptance and Commitment Therapy (ACT) to help you transform your mindset and live more authentically—building on everything you've explored in Radical Acceptance!

Visit this link: https://amzn.to/3WMsnUC
Or scan the QR code on this page.

The Perfect Gift for Teens (and Tweens!)

DBT Skills Workbook for Teens

A Fun and Highly Relatable Workbook for Teens to Manage Difficult Emotions, Cope with Teen Stress & Create Better Friendships

Includes 60+ Engaging Worksheets!

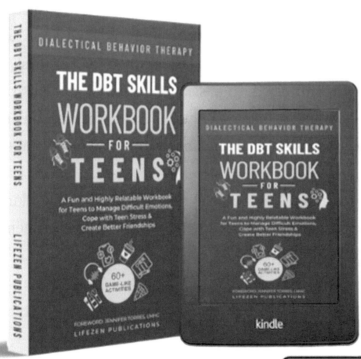

Click here to get your DBT copy now:
https://life-zen.com/dbt
Or scan the QR code on this page.

About the Author

Ava Walters is the founder of LifeZen Publications. Coming from a family with a history of mental health issues, her journey began as a personal quest to find balance, inner peace, and what we all desire—happiness. This pursuit has led her to explore traditional psychotherapeutic methods and diverse holistic practices.

She has an MBA with a specialization in International Project Management (IPM). However, her trajectory took a significant turn after experiencing "a burnout and a breakdown." She then returned to her first love—writing, complementing it with her deep passion for psychology. This transformation marked the beginning of her new journey. One focused on unraveling the intricate connections between human behavior and mental healing.

When she's not writing, Ava can be found on her yoga mat, taking long nature walks with her husband, or in the kitchen, constantly experimenting with new recipes to her husband's delight.

Learn more about Ava and LifeZen Publications here:
https://life-zen.com/

Index

References

1 Linehan, M. (2015). *DBT Skills Training Manual*. Guilford Press.

2 Killingsworth, M. A., & Gilbert, D. T. (2010). A wandering mind is an unhappy mind. *Science, 330*(6006), 932–932. https://doi.org/10.1126/science.1192439

3 Figueiredo, T., Lima, G., Erthal, P., Martins, R., Corção, P., Leonel, M., Ayrão, V., Fortes, D., & Mattos, P. (2020). Mind-wandering, depression, anxiety and ADHD: Disentangling the relationship. *Psychiatry Research, 285*, 112798. https://doi.org/10.1016/j.psychres.2020.112798

4 Ray, J. (2022, June 28). *World Unhappier, more stressed out than ever.* Gallup.com. https://news.gallup.com/poll/394025/world-unhappier-stressed-ever.aspx

5 Desai, R. (2020, August 28). *Stress has made us shallow breathers. here's what it does to our bodies.* The Swaddle. https://www.theswaddle.com/stress-has-made-us-shallow-breathers-heres-what-it-does-to-our-bodies

6 *Deep vs shallow breathing - causes, dangers, benefits, exercises.* Buteyko Clinic International. (2020, December 9). https://buteykoclinic.com/deep-vs-shallow-breathing-causes-dangers-benefits-exercises/

7 Zaccaro, A., Piarulli, A., Laurino, M., Garbella, E., Menicucci, D., Neri, B., & Gemignani, A. (2018). How breath-control can change your life: A systematic review on psycho-physiological correlates of slow breathing.

Frontiers in Human Neuroscience, 12.
https://doi.org/10.3389/fnhum.2018.00353

8 Langshur, E., & Klemp, N. J. (2018). *Start here: Master the lifelong habit of Wellbeing.* Gallery Books.

9 Brownlee, D. (2020, January 15). *Doing this at least 10 minutes a day could transform your productivity.* Forbes.
https://www.forbes.com/sites/danabrownlee/2020/01/15/doing-this-at-least-10-minutes-a-day-could-transform-your-productivity/

10 Knox, R. (2018, April 6). *Harvard study: Clearing your mind affects your genes and can lower your blood pressure.* WBUR News.
https://www.wbur.org/news/2018/04/06/harvard-study-relax-genes

11 Khoury, B., Lecomte, T., Fortin, G., Masse, M., Therien, P., Bouchard, V., Chapleau, M.-A., Paquin, K., & Hofmann, S. G. (2013). Mindfulness-based therapy: A comprehensive meta-analysis. *Clinical Psychology Review, 33*(6), 763–771. https://doi.org/10.1016/j.cpr.2013.05.005

12 Black, D. S., & Slavich, G. M. (2016). Mindfulness meditation and the immune system: A systematic review of randomized controlled trials. *Annals of the New York Academy of Sciences, 1373*(1), 13–24.
https://doi.org/10.1111/nyas.12998

13 Carrière, K., Khoury, B., Günak, M. M., & Knäuper, B. (2017). Mindfulness-based interventions for weight loss: A systematic review and meta-analysis. *Obesity Reviews, 19*(2), 164–177.
https://doi.org/10.1111/obr.12623

14 Rusch, H. L., Rosario, M., Levison, L. M., Olivera, A., Livingston, W. S., Wu, T., & Gill, J. M. (2018). The effect of mindfulness meditation on sleep

quality: A systematic review and meta-analysis of randomized controlled trials. *Annals of the New York Academy of Sciences, 1445*(1), 5–16. https://doi.org/10.1111/nyas.13996

15 Zeidan, F., Johnson, S. K., Diamond, B. J., David, Z., & Goolkasian, P. (2010). Mindfulness meditation improves cognition: Evidence of brief mental training. *Consciousness and Cognition, 19*(2), 597–605. https://doi.org/10.1016/j.concog.2010.03.014

16 Schertz, K. E., & Berman, M. G. (2019). Understanding nature and its cognitive benefits. *Current Directions in Psychological Science, 28*(5), 496–502. https://doi.org/10.1177/0963721419854100

17 Robbins, J. (2020, January 9). *Ecopsychology: How immersion in nature benefits your health.* Yale E360. https://e360.yale.edu/features/ecopsychology-how-immersion-in-nature-benefits-your-health

18 Jimenez, M. P., DeVille, N. V., Elliott, E. G., Schiff, J. E., Wilt, G. E., Hart, J. E., & James, P. (2021). Associations between Nature Exposure and Health: A review of the evidence. *International Journal of Environmental Research and Public Health, 18*(9), 4790. https://doi.org/10.3390/ijerph18094790

19 Lerner, J. S., Li, Y., Valdesolo, P., & Kassam, K. S. (2015). Emotion and decision making. *Annual Review of Psychology, 66*(1), 799–823. https://doi.org/10.1146/annurev-psych-010213-115043

20 Sifferlin, A. (2014, August 6). *Trustworthiness: Your brain makes a judgment in milliseconds.* Time. https://time.com/3083667/brain-trustworthiness/

21 Forsythe, F. (2019, February 20). *Why judging others is our natural instinct, Harvard Psychologist explains*. Learning Mind. https://www.learning-mind.com/judging-others/

22 Ortet, G., Pinazo, D., Walker, D., Gallego, S., Mezquita, L., & Ibáñez, M. I. (2020). Personality and nonjudging make you happier: Contribution of the five-factor model, mindfulness facets and a mindfulness intervention to subjective well-being. *PLOS ONE, 15*(2). https://doi.org/10.1371/journal.pone.0228655

23 Shahar, G. (2017, August 9). *The hazards of self-criticism*. Psychology Today. https://www.psychologytoday.com/us/blog/stress-self-and-health/201708/the-hazards-self-criticism

24 McIntyre, R., Smith, P., & Rimes, K. A. (2018). The role of self-criticism in common mental health difficulties in students: A systematic review of prospective studies. *Mental Health and Prevention, 10*, 13–27. https://doi.org/10.1016/j.mhp.2018.02.003

25 Warren, R., Smeets, E., & Neff, K. (2016, December). *Self-criticism and self-compassion: Risk and resilience*. Self-Compassion. https://self-compassion.org/wp-content/uploads/2016/12/Self-Criticism.pdf

26 Doan, T., Ha, V., Strazdins, L., & Chateau, D. (2022). Healthy minds live in healthy bodies – effect of physical health on Mental Health: Evidence from Australian Longitudinal Data. *Current Psychology, 42*(22), 18702–18713. https://doi.org/10.1007/s12144-022-03053-7

27 Mahindru, A., Patil, P., & Agrawal, V. (2023). Role of physical activity on mental health and well-being: A Review. *Cureus*. https://doi.org/10.7759/cureus.33475

28 John, S. N. (2013). *The Book of Afformations: Discovering the Missing Piece to Abundant Health, Wealth, Love, and Happiness.* Hay House.

29 Childs, J. H., & Stoeber, J. (2012). Do you want me to be perfect? Two longitudinal studies on socially prescribed perfectionism, stress and burnout in the Workplace. *Work and Stress, 26*(4), 347–364. https://doi.org/10.1080/02678373.2012.737547

30 Smith, M. M., Sherry, S. B., McLarnon, M. E., Flett, G. L., Hewitt, P. L., Saklofske, D. H., & Etherson, M. E. (2018). Why does socially prescribed perfectionism place people at risk for depression? A five-month, two-wave longitudinal study of the perfectionism social disconnection model. *Personality and Individual Differences, 134,* 49–54. https://doi.org/10.1016/j.paid.2018.05.040

31 *Embracing body positivity linked to a happier life, Global Study reveals.* Mind Help. (2023, September 5). https://mind.help/news/mental-health-and-happiness/

32 Nummenmaa, L., Glerean, E., Hari, R., & Hietanen, J. K. (2013). Bodily maps of emotions. *Proceedings of the National Academy of Sciences, 111*(2), 646–651. https://doi.org/10.1073/pnas.1321664111

33 Kaleja, L. (2021, January 6). *Self-forgiveness for most people is harder than to forgive others.* Medium. https://medium.com/better-advice/self-forgiveness-for-most-people-is-harder-than-to-forgive-others-6419537d42d2

34 Macaskill, A. (2012). Differentiating dispositional self-forgiveness from other-forgiveness: Associations with mental health and life satisfaction. *Journal of Social and Clinical Psychology, 31*(1), 28–50. https://doi.org/10.1521/jscp.2012.31.1.28

35 Gendlin, E. T. (2007). *Focusing*. Bantam.

36 Guilfoyle, J. R., Struthers, C. W., van Monsjou, E., & Shoikhedbrod, A. (2019). Sorry is the hardest word to say: The role of self-control in apologizing. *Basic and Applied Social Psychology*, *41*(1), 72–90. https://doi.org/10.1080/01973533.2018.1553715

37 Northwestern Medicine. (2021, September). *5 benefits of healthy relationships*. https://www.nm.org/healthbeat/healthy-tips/5-benefits-of-healthy-relationships

38 Firth, J., Torous, J., Stubbs, B., Firth, J. A., Steiner, G. Z., Smith, L., Alvarez-Jimenez, M., Gleeson, J., Vancampfort, D., Armitage, C. J., & Sarris, J. (2019). The "Online Brain": How the internet may be changing our cognition. *World Psychiatry*, *18*(2), 119–129. https://doi.org/10.1002/wps.20617

39 Thomas, S. (2023, July 4). *How social media changes our perception of reality*. Insight Digital Magazine. https://www.thechicagoschool.edu/insight/from-the-magazine/a-virtual-life/

40 *The importance of learning and growing your knowledge - beautiful minds*. Beautiful Minds®. (2022, October 12). https://beautifulminds.com.au/the-importance-of-learning-and-growing-your-knowledge/

41 Brower, T. (2021, October 17). *Learning is a sure path to happiness: Science proves it*. Forbes. https://www.forbes.com/sites/tracybrower/2021/10/17/learning-is-a-sure-path-to-happiness-science-proves-it/

42 Otake, K., Shimai, S., Tanaka-Matsumi, J., Otsui, K., & Fredrickson, B. L. (2006). Happy people become happier through kindness: A counting kindnesses intervention. *Journal of Happiness Studies*, *7*(3), 361–375. https://doi.org/10.1007/s10902-005-3650-z

43 Emmons, R. A., & McCullough, M. E. (2003). Counting blessings versus burdens: An experimental investigation of gratitude and subjective well-being in daily life. *Journal of Personality and Social Psychology*, *84*(2), 377–389. https://doi.org/10.1037/0022-3514.84.2.377

Made in United States
Troutdale, OR
10/26/2024

24141239R00097